"I don't want to have this baby in the middle of Highway 81,"

Maddie said to the stranger, panic racing through her. "Listen, I'll cook you dinner for a year if you'll just take me to the hospital on your motorcycle—"

Another contraction hit. By the time the pain passed, the man was carefully placing a helmet on her head.

"Thank you so very much," she said, fighting tears of relief.

"Save your thank-yous for when you get to the hospital," he muttered before he mounted the bike.

Maddie shot the motorcycle a doubtful look and gingerly straddled it.

"Are you on?"

"Yes," she whispered.

"All I want you to do is hold on. I'm gonna move as quickly and easily as I can. When you feel a contraction coming on, squeeze me, yell at me, kick me—just let me know."

Her opinion of him rose ten feet. He was strong. He was practical.

Most important, he was there.

MARRY ME,
Cowboy

THE TROUBLEMAKER BRIDE

Leanne Banks

Kids
&Kin

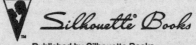

Silhouette Books

Published by Silhouette Books
America's Publisher of Contemporary Romance

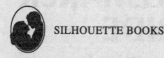

SILHOUETTE BOOKS

ISBN 0-373-65340-9

THE TROUBLEMAKER BRIDE

LEANNE BANKS,

a *USA TODAY* bestselling author of romance novels and 2002 winner of the prestigious Booksellers' Best Award, lives in her native Virginia with her husband, son and daughter. Recognized for both her sensual and humorous writing with two Career Achievement Awards from *Romantic Times*, Leanne likes creating a story with a few grins, a generous kick of sensuality and characters that hang around after the book is finished. Leanne believes romance readers are the best readers in the world because they understand that love is the greatest miracle of all. Contact Leanne online at leannebbb@aol.com or write to her at P.O. Box 1442, Midlothian, VA 23113. A SASE for a reply would be greatly appreciated.

Please address questions and book requests to:
Silhouette Reader Service
U.S.: 3010 Walden Ave., P.O. Box 1325, Buffalo, NY 14269
Canadian: P.O. Box 609, Fort Erie, Ont. L2A 5X3

Special acknowledgments to Margaret, Debbie and Debra for all the fun we had strumming our badminton rackets for our Monkees band practice.

This book is dedicated to the Monkees for giving my little-girl heart its first flutter, and to all the other girls who felt the same way. You guys made daydream believers out of all of us....

Prologue

Nine-year-old Maddie Palmer dropped the needle on the record and made a quick dash for the bar stool. She scrambled onto the seat and stood. "One, two, three, four!" she yelled out just like Davey Rogers of the Pink Bubblegum rock band.

Grinning at her pals, Emily and Jenna Jean, she belted out the opening chorus along with her favorite rock star. Her friends stood on top of the seats of matching brown vinyl bar stools and sang along. Since it was raining on Cherry Lane today, Maddie had talked the baby-sitter into letting her and her friends play in the basement.

Life was good. The baby-sitter let her play the music as loudly as she wanted. She'd just bought the new 45 record spinning on her record player. She was strumming her pretend guitar, a badminton racket, with her two best friends. Maddie was even wearing Emily's fancy tiara. And for once she wasn't grounded.

When the record ended with a loud static sound, Maddie jumped off the stool and ran to the record player. "Let's do it again," she said, holding the tiara in place with her other hand. "If we get good enough, maybe we could put on a show and charge people a quarter to hear us sing."

Dressed in a pink pinafore, Emily looked at her badminton racket doubtfully. "I don't know, Maddie. I don't think I'm a very good rock star."

Jenna Jean bounced her racket against her fist. "I don't know if anyone is gonna pay to see us. We might have to give them food or something. Those creepy boys would just laugh." She looked at Maddie. "Besides, these rackets look more like banjos than electric guitars."

"Well, maybe we could serve fruit punch and cookies," Maddie suggested, ignoring the comment about the badminton rackets since she couldn't do anything about it. She was more worried about her voice. She lived in mortal fear that her singing sounded as bad to others as it did to her, but she was too chicken to ask her friends to tell the truth, so she just sang as loudly as she could.

"Do you really want to be a rock star when you grow up? My mother says they hardly ever take a bath," Emily said with a shudder.

"Davey Rogers of the Pink Bubblegum rock band takes a bath," Maddie insisted. "I know cause I'm an official member of his fan club." Emily was a little bit prissy, but Maddie liked her because she was nice and shared her tiara. "I don't really have to be a rock star. I just want to be rich and go exciting places. I want to have adventures," she told her, then remembered her deepest wish of all. "And never get grounded again."

"I would go crazy if my mom made me stay in my yard as much as yours does," Jenna Jean said, swiveling her bar stool around as she stood on it. "It seems like you're always getting into trouble."

Maddie got a yucky feeling in the pit of her stomach. Sometimes she wondered what was wrong with her. Neither of her friends got grounded as often as she did. "I don't do anything that terrible."

She watched Jenna Jean swivel the chair again and thought about asking her to stop. Jenna Jean was a show-off, and Maddie's mother didn't like it when they stood on the bar stools.

"Nope," Jenna Jean said. "You know what your problem is."

"What?"

"You get caught."

The yucky feeling in her stomach got worse. Jenna Jean was a whole year older, and she was very smart. She even got As in Math. Maddie got Cs.

"Maybe," she admitted. "Maybe I'm just bad." Maddie didn't like to think about how often she got grounded. Hands on her hips, she turned to her friends. "Come on. While my mom's gone, let's practice this song again and pretend we're singing at the coliseum downtown."

She dropped the needle on the record and scrambled on top of the chair again. Her hands poised to strum the badminton racket, her mouth open and ready to sing, she watched her mother enter the basement.

Maddie froze in horror.

Out of the corner of her eye, she saw Jenna Jean and Emily scramble off their stools, but Maddie couldn't seem to move her feet as her mother took in the scene with a disapproving expression.

"Young lady," her mother said, and Maddie sighed. Whenever her mother called her young lady, she was grounded.

"What are you doing standing on that bar stool?

I've told you a dozen times not to stand on the bar stools. What if you or your friends got hurt?'' She shook her finger at Maddie. ''You've had your warning, now...''

Maddie glanced at Jenna Jean as her mother went on with her lecture. *Caught* again.

One

Maddie stared outside her car window. The same sight greeted her from all sides. Cars. Stopped cars.

She was in the middle of a traffic jam on Highway 81.

Caught again.

This sort of thing didn't happen in Roanoke, Virginia. The population wasn't dense enough to create a traffic problem, especially not on the highway. According to the radio, however, a sinkhole had given way smack dab in the middle lane, causing expected delays of up to two hours.

It might have been okay if she were in the right-hand lane and could use the curb to reach her destination, but she was in the middle lane. It wasn't as if she was in a rush to get to her job as a travel agent. She had taken the day off. It wasn't as if she had a pressing dinner date either. She hadn't been on a dinner date in about nine months.

Her problem was the rhythmic tightening of the muscles in her back and abdomen, slowly building, then peaking. More discomfort than pain, the tightening occurred every five minutes. Maddie kept telling herself the feeling would go away, but she suspected she was in labor. In the middle of the only traffic jam in the history of Roanoke, Virginia. In the rain. With no car phone.

Her stomach growled, and she wished for the fortieth time that she'd brought some cookies in the car with her. Another contraction hit, this one requiring the use of a breathing technique. Maddie visualized Maui, beautiful water, palm trees, rainbows. If she were in Maui, she would be sipping a Mai Tai. God knows, she could use something with liquor in it right now.

A thread of panic raced through her. She really didn't want to have her baby in the middle of a highway. Turning on her windshield wipers, she searched desperately for a patrol car. This was one time she would gladly face a policeman. Unfortunately none were around.

Desperation sank in. Maybe she should get out and walk. But hadn't her natural-childbirth instructor said that walking hurried labor along? What if she didn't make it far enough to find a ride to the hospital?

Through the light rain she spotted a pickup truck with a motorcycle covered in plastic in its bed. An insane idea struck her. Insane as it seemed, was it any crazier than delivering a baby in her car by herself?

Going with her instincts, Maddie awkwardly got out of her green convertible and waddled past two cars to the driver's window of the truck. She knocked on the foggy window.

The man inside turned his head to stare at her.

She smiled.

He didn't.

Maddie sighed and motioned for him to roll down his window.

"Yes?" he asked in a voice that sent a shiver down her spine. His radio played a heavy metal song, and it appeared there was someone in the passenger seat, but she couldn't be sure.

Maddie looked at the man and bit her lip. Though he was seated, he looked big and forbidding, and about as flexible as steel. His eyes were cool gray, his face angular and chiseled. Her long-time friend Jenna Jean was always telling Maddie that she jumped to conclusions about people, but this man didn't look friendly. He didn't look like he had much of a sense of humor. Under other circumstances she would turn around and go back to her car. The only thing she needed more than a sense of humor right now, though, was this man's motorcycle.

"I—uh—" Another contraction hit, and she held up her hand. "Just a minute, please," she whispered, and focused on the door handle. Inhale. Exhale. Inhale. Exhale.

Alarm cracked his features. "What in—"

With an effort she straightened after the peak. "Does the motorcycle in the back of your truck work?"

"Yes, but—"

"I know this is unusual," she said in a rush, because she wanted to voice her request before another contraction hit. "But I'm in labor and I need to get to a hospital before—"

A gush of water spilled down her legs. Maddie stared at her drenched tennis shoes. "Oh, damn."

"Damn?"

"My water broke," she said, and met his wary gaze. Maybe he was human after all. When he wasn't glaring, he was almost attractive. She reassessed him. At second glance, he still looked a bit grim, but responsible, she thought hopefully. The strength stamped across his features appealed to her. And with those shoulders, she'd bet he had a killer body. In other circumstances she might have— Maddie looked at her watermelon stomach and dismissed the thought. "Can I borrow your motorcycle, please?"

The radio volume lowered. "Dad, who's standing outside—" The younger male voice abruptly stopped. "It's a pregnant lady," he said, his voice cracking in adolescent surprise.

Dad didn't answer his son's question. In one swift motion he was out of the car, staring down at Maddie. "Let me get this straight. You want me to take you to the hospital on a motorcycle?"

She nodded and covered her abdomen protectively. "I don't think I have much choice. I don't want to have this baby on Highway 81." When he didn't immediately respond, she felt a slice of panic. What if he didn't help her? She clasped her fingers together. "Listen, I don't have a lot of money, but you can have it." He shook his head. "I'm a travel agent. Maybe I could arrange a free trip for you. Or I can cook," she said, feeling desperation thicken her throat. "I'll cook you a dinner a week for a year if you'll just—"

Another contraction hit, and the pain made her double over. In the middle of it she heard some tersely worded instructions. By the time the pain passed, the motorcycle was out of the truck, and the son had slid over to the driver's seat. Fighting tears of relief, Maddie gave the wide-eyed teenage boy a weak smile.

"Miss—" the man began awkwardly.

"Maddie, Maddie Palmer," she told him, extending her hand.

His large, warm hand swallowed hers. "Joshua Blackwell," he said, his face tight with concern. "Can you make it to the side of the road?"

She nodded. "Yes, thank you so much."

Joshua walked behind her. "Save your thank-yous for when you get to the hospital," he muttered, carefully placing a helmet on her head, then another on his, before he mounted the bike.

Maddie shot the motorcycle a doubtful look and gingerly straddled it. Motorcycles were not designed for pregnant women. Biting her lip, she stretched her arms around her bulk to his waist and held on tight.

"Are you on?"

"Yes," she whispered, wrestling with another contraction.

"How far apart are they?"

Maddie waited until the pain passed. "Under four minutes."

"Great," he muttered. "All I want you to do is hold on. I'm gonna move as quick and easy as I can. When you feel a contraction coming on, squeeze me, yell at me, kick me—just let me know.''

Her opinion of Joshua rose ten feet. He was strong. He was practical. Most importantly, he was there. ''Okay.''

He nodded shortly and started the motor. ''Let's go.''

They made it to the hospital in seventeen minutes and thirty-two seconds. Joshua was counting. It must have been a helluva ride for Maddie. By the time they arrived, her face was pinched and drawn. She practically fell off the bike. The ER crew helped her into a wheelchair and took her up to delivery, shouting instructions at Joshua to follow.

He'd never been one to blindly follow instructions, but this time he did. Driving a red-haired pregnant lady to the hospital set his adrenaline humming. He washed up, dressed in a sterile paper coverall and was directed to the birthing room.

''Hi,'' she said, her voice laced with relief as he walked through the door. ''They say my o.b. doctor won't get here in time.''

He frowned. ''What about your husband?''

''I don't have one,'' she said, and looked away. Joshua took a long look at her. Her face pale against the drab hospital gown, she looked young and scared. Aside from the massive bulk at her midriff, her body was small-boned and delicate. He felt a strange wave of protectiveness, and despite the odd circumstances, assessed her again. Her breasts were full, her legs shapely. He couldn't venture a guess about her hips, since they weren't visible. But he would guess she was usually slim.

Freckles on her nose, wary curiosity in her brown eyes, she watched him watching her. The tilt of her chin told him she was a fighter. Something about her mouth told him she was a woman of passion, and Joshua felt a flicker of curiosity.

"You don't have to stay if you don't want to," she told him.

Struck by a rare moment of indecision, Joshua stifled a curse when Maddie closed her eyes and began to breathe deeply.

Her face crinkled in pain and she shook her head. "I need to push. Go get the nur— No!" she choked out and reached for him when he turned. "Stay."

He let her grab on to his hand. For a small woman, she squeezed him tighter than a vise grip. "Pant," he told her, dimly recalling his experience with the birth of his son sixteen years ago. "Pant."

Wonder of wonders, Maddie complied, panting until the urge to push passed. When Joshua tried to withdraw his hand, she shook her head, her eyes wide with fear.

His heart twisted, the sensation strange, nearly forgotten. "I'll be back in less than thirty seconds. I promise."

Her gaze meshed with his, and he saw the second she trusted him. It gave him a rush, but he shook it off. He would have to think about that later. A baby was waiting to be born.

True to his word, Joshua returned swiftly, with a nurse in tow. Everything happened quickly after the nurse examined Maddie. "Don't push. You'll tear. I'll find the doctor."

"Where is he?" Maddie demanded. "Drinking coffee and eating donuts. I swear, men are never around when you need them."

Talking more to herself than anyone else, she grimaced as another contraction hit, cursing all of mankind. "You wouldn't think one little hole in— a—condom—" She broke off and sobbed. "Could-cause-this-much-pain," she finished in a rush.

"Maui," she murmured to herself. "S'posed to visualize something pleasant. Maui. If I were in Maui, I'd be snorkeling off of Molokini. I'd be—" She stopped and screamed. "Where is the doctor?"

Joshua took her hand and held it even when her

nails bit into his skin. The doctor finally appeared, and Maddie pushed for twenty-three tense minutes before her squalling baby boy made his appearance. The nurse wrapped the baby and laid him on Maddie's chest.

"He's beautiful," she said, tears streaming down her cheeks. "He's just beautiful." She touched his pointy bald head and smoothed his crumpled ears. "You were in a hurry, weren't you?" she cooed.

The moment was so intimate it was hard for Joshua to watch. Suddenly feeling superfluous, he swiped the perspiration from his forehead and thought about making his exit.

The movement must have caught her attention. Maddie glanced up at him. Sniffing loudly, she smiled through her tears. "He's beautiful, isn't he?"

Joshua looked at the baby and twisted his mouth. "Yeah, he's something else."

"Want to hold him?"

Nonplussed, he hesitated.

"Go ahead," she urged, tilting the bundle toward him.

Joshua moved forward and gingerly took the baby in his arms. So small, so fragile, but so alive. He looked at the little human being staring back at him. The baby waved his fist in the air.

Joshua thought of Patrick. He'd always done his best for his son in his wife's absence, but during the long years of his struggle to do the right thing, something inside him had just died. Despite his best efforts, he knew Patrick had needed something from him that he just couldn't give. So it was with a great sense of shock, that after twelve years out in the cold, Joshua felt a rush of warmth. The sensation was so unfamiliar he didn't know what to do with it.

A nurse rushed into the room. "Ms. Palmer, the people you asked us to notify are in the waiting room and are quite insistent about seeing you. Mr. Benjamin Palmer—"

"My brother," Maddie said. "And I'll bet the other is Jenna Jean."

"Ms. Jenna Anderson," the nurse said.

"Tell them I'll see them in a few minutes and," she added, a trace of mischief mingling with the weary joy in her eyes. "Tell them I had quintuplets."

The nurse's jaw dropped, and she glanced at the baby in Joshua's arms. "Pardon me."

"It's just for fun," Maddie said. "They've agreed to be the godparents." She chuckled, then looked up at Joshua and the baby. Her eyes softened. "Bet when you woke up this morning you had no idea you'd be rescuing a pregnant lady from a sinkhole and helping deliver a baby."

"Can't say I did," he said, thinking she had more exuberance in her little finger than he had in his entire body. He felt the sting of envy and unwilling attraction. The double pop of unfamiliar emotion unsettled him. "Here he is," Joshua said, bending to return the baby to Maddie.

She held the baby against her chest in a natural maternal way. In a move just as natural, she extended one hand and urged Joshua closer. "Come here," she said, and surprised the hell out of him by kissing him right next to his mouth. "Thanks. You were a hero today."

He stared into her warm gaze and felt a weird shift inside him. Blinking, he backed away and cleared his throat. "No problem," he muttered. "I should go. You take care of the kid. And take care of you, too," he said, feeling a grudging acceptance that he was walking out of Maddie Palmer's life.

Joshua didn't remember the exact day he'd stopped dreaming. He just knew he hadn't dreamed during his sleep in years.

When Joshua slid between the covers of his big bed that night, he didn't expect any dreams. He listened to the silence in his house. It was a good silence, he told himself. Especially after the noise of the day.

He thought about the schedule he'd set for bringing in mares and getting them settled. He thought about his teenage son and how each day seemed to bring a little more distance between them. It disturbed him, but Joshua knew Patrick was growing up, and growing up meant pulling apart from his dad.

His mind eased back to the picture of Maddie with her newborn son, prompting a memory of the day Patrick was born. He and his wife had been far too young for the responsibility of raising a child, but they'd accepted that responsibility, anyway.

They'd both been full of hope and full of dreams.

That had been before Gail got sick. Before she faded away before his eyes and died. Patrick had only been four years old.

Sometime after that Joshua stopped dreaming. It was okay, he told himself. He had work to do, and he had to fumble his way through being a single parent. Life was serious business. For Joshua there was no time for dreams.

Two

Early evening at the Blackwell's ranch home, and it was quiet. Joshua thumbed through the newspaper. The only noises were restless noises, the rustling of his paper, his son's foot tapping against the kitchen chair as he did his homework, and his German shepherd, Major, prowling around the front door.

He was accustomed to the absence of noise. If he allowed himself to think about it, Joshua could nail the emotion the quiet provoked—emptiness. But Joshua was a busy man with the responsibilities of managing a successful horse farm and raising his teenage son by himself. There wasn't time to dwell on what was missing.

He glanced over his newspaper at Patrick. He suspected Patrick viewed him as a stern, humorless and cold man. A sliver of doubt cut through, and Joshua wondered if indeed he had become that kind of man.

Dismissing the unproductive thought, he glanced back at his paper and ignored the distance between his son and him. But the quiet, the endless, empty quiet, remained.

Major growled.

"Lay down," Joshua commanded.

Major obeyed for a quarter minute, then rose again and started barking. Patrick glanced up from his homework. "What's his problem?"

Joshua shrugged, getting up to let the dog out. As soon as he opened the door, he heard the distinctive sound of a muffler in need of repair. The muffler was attached to a car making its way down the dirt road to his house. Major was barking his fool head off as Joshua squinted his eyes against the evening darkness. He flicked on the outside lights. The car was vaguely familiar, but he couldn't quite remember...

The green convertible pulled to a jerky stop right in front of his house. A moment later the driver's car door opened, and the sound of a screaming baby joined Major's chorus.

Patrick joined Joshua. "What…"

The two Blackwell males watched in amazement as Maddie Palmer put her baby in a pouch she wore on the front of her, grabbed two large baskets and stomped past Major up the steps.

"Hi," she said cheerily, her brown eyes glinting with the same good humor as her uptilted mouth. "Remember me? You gave me a ride to the hospital six weeks ago and helped deliver my baby. I promised a meal a week for the next year, and I try to keep my promises. So, here's your first one."

"Excuse me?" Joshua said, staring at her in disbelief. She didn't actually think he could have forgotten her. He sure as hell had never driven any other pregnant women to the hospital on the back of his motorcycle.

"Food," Patrick said, his voice nearly trembling with joy. "She brought food, Dad."

"This isn't nec—"

She lifted her shoulders in a half shrug. "Already done."

As the baby started to fuss, Joshua and Patrick took the baskets. "This really isn't—" Joshua began again.

"There's a pie!" Patrick shouted as if he hadn't seen one in years.

"Come in," Joshua said as the baby got louder.

"I underestimated how long it would take me to find you," she told him as she followed him toward the sofa. "Plus I got lost and had to ask one of your neighbors for directions. Mr. Crockett. He's a crabby one, isn't he?"

"You stopped at Otis Crockett's house?" Patrick asked, his attention veering momentarily from the food to Maddie. "Did he pull a gun on you?"

"He didn't exactly point it at me," Maddie said, freeing her fussing son from the pouch. "But he had it over his shoulder and he wasn't helpful. I told him he needed to work on his language. It could strip wallpaper."

"Oh, God," Joshua muttered under his breath, feeling a thud of uneasiness in his gut. Maddie looked so helpless and Otis enjoyed firing guns. "Don't stop at Otis Crockett's house. He's been to court for his temper before."

"He needs a personality makeover," she said over the baby's wail.

"Don't stop at—" For emphasis, Joshua started to repeat himself, but broke off when he saw Maddie pull her shirt from her waistband.

His expression must have stopped her. She paused and lifted her shoulder. "Studmuffin, here, is way overdue for his feeding. I'm sure it's nothing you've never seen before, but—"

"In the kitchen, Patrick," Joshua said, immediately turning around and walking away. He rubbed the back of his neck and shook his head. Stifling an oath, he motioned for his son to sit facing away from Maddie as she nursed her baby.

"Dad, it's not that big of a deal. It's natural."

"Tell someone else, Patrick. I was sixteen once." He began to understand why most hurricanes were named after women. In less than two minutes, Maddie had walked into his quiet peaceful home and turned it upside down.

He pulled the dishes from the baskets and served the food, noting the baby's silence. That meant Studmuffin was being fed, and Maddie's breasts were bare. Nothing to get worked up about, Joshua told himself. As Patrick had said, it was natural. But it had been a long time since a woman had sat in his den, longer still since a woman with bare breasts had sat there.

Joshua deliberately cleared the image from his head and focused on the food. It was much better than the scrambled eggs he'd planned.

"This is great," Patrick said as he reached for another piece of fried chicken.

"Enjoy it," Joshua told him dryly. "It'll be your last great meal for a while."

"Not that long," Maddie said from behind him.

He jerked his head to look up at her, taking note

of her rearranged clothing and then her smile. Her smile was slightly crooked, but generous and appealing enough to hold his attention. He lifted his eyebrows. "Not that long?"

"That's right," she said, as she gently patted the baby on the back. "I promised you one meal a week for a year."

He immediately rejected the idea. "That's not necessary. It was nice of you to bring this tonight, but let's call it even with this one," he said, ignoring Patrick's protest. "It's not practical or reasonable for you to bring a home-cooked meal all the way out here every week."

Maddie's smile grew wider. "It wasn't really practical or reasonable for you to drive a pregnant woman to the hospital on the back of your motorcycle, then stay with her during the delivery of her baby, either, was it?"

"I—"

"That's an excellent point," Patrick said.

Joshua clamped his mouth shut. Between his son, the bottomless teenage pit, and Hurricane Maddie, he could see he was going to have to be firm. "It's not—"

"I should leave," she said, gathering her basket and a few of the empty dishes. "Maui's a little temperamental, and since I don't know my way around your neighborhood in the daylight, let alone the dark, I'd hate to get stranded.''

Thoroughly confused, Joshua stood. "Maui?"

"Oh, that's what I named my car. A couple of years ago I had to choose between taking a trip to Maui and buying a new car. I chose Maui and decided to call my car that as a reminder every time it broke down.'' Glancing down at her sleeping baby, she shook her head. "Didn't you hear what I told you last night?'' she whispered. "You're supposed to wait for me before you go to sleep.''

The baby didn't stir.

Maddie tossed Joshua and Patrick a wry glance. "Men.''

Patrick laughed. "Did you, uh, really name him Studmuffin?''

Her eyes widened. "Oh, no. His name is David. A good solid name to make up for having an eccentric mother. Single mother,'' she added under her breath, and the light in her eyes dimmed just a little as if she knew the responsibility of raising a child would be a lonely venture at times.

She gave the appearance of being a damn-the-torpedoes kind of woman, carefree, full of husky laughter that made Joshua think of early mornings in bed. With her casually tossed red hair and mischievous brown eyes, a man might conclude she was a little wild. In his quiet, orderly world, she was noisy and disruptive. She was friendly, but she gave the impression she was at ease with her own sexuality. It was in the way she moved, the way she talked, the way she met his gaze. She made him uncomfortable.

"Like I said, I should go. Anything you don't like besides liver?" she asked as she headed for the door. "I aim to please."

Joshua felt a tug in his stomach and blinked. "Please," he echoed, his pulse kicking as his mind registered a swift, inappropriate, but scorching image.

She nodded. "Dinner next week. Thanks, Patrick," she said, walking onto the front porch.

"Thank you, Miss—"

"Maddie," she told him. "Just Maddie."

Joshua desperately needed to get control of the situation. "Let me take that," he said, and carried the basket to the car. A light drizzle fell. He opened the car door, and she fastened her baby in the car seat.

"Maddie," he began when she stood. "It was nice of you to bring the meal—"

"You're welcome."

Unaccustomed to being interrupted by a distractingly attractive woman, he paused a half beat before he got the conversation back on track. "It's not necessary for you to bring a meal every week. Not necessary, not practical, not reasonable.''

She gave that husky chuckle again, and it shimmied down his nerve endings to flick across his masculinity. "Not practical, not reasonable. Thank goodness there are lots of things that aren't reasonable and practical. And I would argue about whether it's necessary or not."

She shook her head and leaned closer. She didn't intend it as an invitation. It was merely her natural body language, he knew, yet his fingers curled at the urge to just touch her. "I'm not used to being rescued by solid, dependable, conservative ranchers. I'm not used to being rescued at all. I need to say thank you. Do me a favor and just enjoy the meals. Okay?"

Speechless, he expelled a breath of frustration.

"I'll take that as a yes." She walked to the driver's side of the car and smiled just before she got in. "G'night, Joshua Blackwell."

"G'night," he muttered after she closed her door.

Her engine coughed to life, with the muffler buzzing loudly. He could barely hear himself think over the noise of her car, but he noticed Major started barking again, another animal howled in the distance, and the birds fussed at the interruption.

Even the insects screamed as if they were on edge. Hell, the woman was an assault against nature.

In the evening mist, he watched her drive halfway down the lane. Her car rolled unevenly to a stop. It started to rain harder and Joshua sighed. The night wasn't over yet.

Maddie knew all too well why her car was listing to one side. She had a flat tire. "It's not all bad. This time I have a spare. And the baby is sleeping," she told herself, recalling that the last time she'd had a flat tire she'd held up a funeral procession and David had been fully, noisily, unhappily awake.

She pushed open her car door and stepped into a mud puddle. "This is just another one of life's adventures. It will make me a better person," she chanted under her breath. She'd been chanting the same verse the past ten years of her life and she was still looking forward to the day when she might actually believe it.

Rounding the corner of her car, she plowed into an immovable object. She blinked, then recognized Joshua. "Oh, bet you thought I was gone," she said with a sheepish smile. "You know what they say about bad pennies. Just can't get rid of them. You can go back to your house. I'm an old hand at changing tires."

She opened the trunk, and he grabbed the spare

and jack before she did. Motherhood was making her slow, she thought irritably. "Listen, it's raining. I don't expect you to—"

"Why don't you sit in the car so you won't get wet? It won't take me but a minute," Joshua said, already kneeling beside the deflated tire.

Unaccustomed to having anyone do much of anything for her, Maddie felt uncomfortable. "This is really nice of you, but I can do it. You don't need to. You can—"

He looked up at her. "You sound like I did a few minutes ago."

Even in the dark the intensity of his gray eyes cut through her. Shutting her mouth, Maddie felt her discomfort grow. She'd never favored quiet men, especially those who refused to hold up their end of the conversation. She'd always preferred to spend her time with verbally expressive males, because she wasn't left wondering what they were thinking.

Joshua made her wonder. He was one of those salt-of-the-earth types who probably disapproved of her, but was either too reticent or polite to show it. And she would bet a year's supply of lottery tickets that he was a stick-in-the-mud.

A nice stick-in-the-mud, she amended because the man was changing her tire for her, but still a stick-in-the-mud. He looked like he needed some-

body to loosen him up. She wondered if he had a
sex life, if for that matter, he'd been kissed lately.
The man looked like he needed a kiss.

Maddie felt a nudge of excitement at the same
time she heard a warning bell. She was well familiar with the results of following that nudge of
excitement. She'd gotten herself into trouble too
many times to count, because she'd followed it.
Well she wouldn't be fulfilling any kissing assignments for Joshua Blackwell, she told herself as she
glanced in the car. She checked on David, who was
still sleeping peacefully, then returned to Joshua's
side.

She wished she had an umbrella handy to hold
over him. Damp from the rain, his cotton shirt
faithfully followed the contours of his broad shoulders, back and biceps. She would have to be blind
not to appreciate the strength of his body. But the
appeal was more than physical. For Maddie there
was something insidiously seductive about a man
who had clearly made it through some tough times.

Dependability. She swallowed her chuckle. Who
would have ever thought Maddie Palmer would
find dependability sexy? Her hormones must still
be messed up from the pregnancy.

"Your son seems like a good kid. I bet you're
proud of him," she said to break the quiet and
interrupt her train of thought.

"Yeah," Joshua murmured as he continued working with the tire.

"Is he girl crazy yet?"

Joshua paused, glancing up at her. "If he is, he's keeping it a secret."

His voice was low and deep, wholly masculine, making her want to hear it more. How interesting, she thought, that a straight-and-narrow man could have such an appealing voice. "Academic type, huh?"

"Yeah."

She rolled her eyes. Stingy, stingy, stingy. "Plays his hand close to the vest?"

He nodded.

"Like his dad?"

He paused again and looked at her. "I guess so. I hadn't thought about it before."

That didn't surprise her. He didn't strike her as the kind to sit around and ruminate over his similarities with his son.

"You should have waited in the car," he told her as he lowered the jack. "You got wet."

Maddie glanced at her damp shirt. At the same time she knew her hair was probably sticking out in ten different directions from the moisture. She shrugged. "So did you."

He put the spare and jack in the trunk. "I thought women didn't like to get wet."

"Depends on the reason," she said. "Getting wet in the swimming pool or shower isn't bad. Getting wet because you're standing in line to get tickets for a concert isn't too bad."

He turned to her, and she could have sworn she saw his lips twitch. "What about getting wet because of a flat tire?"

His hair was damp, too, and for a fleeting second, Maddie couldn't help but imagine what Joshua would look like coming out of a morning shower. His body was clearly well-toned and muscular. The image dragged at her stomach, and she blinked to clear it from her mind. "Getting wet because of a flat tire? Depends on how much of an adventure it turns out to be."

His mouth tilted slightly, and he regarded her curiously. "Adventure in a dirt driveway?"

"Sometimes you have to make your own adventures," she told him, and sighed. "Now, how am I going to thank you for this? More meals?"

His eyes widened in dismay and she laughed. "Are you afraid of a bad penny? Do you want to put the flat tire back on?"

"No," he said immediately, without conviction.

"But you thought about it," she said, and laughed.

"How about a simple thank-you?" Joshua suggested.

The man looked like he needed to be kissed. The impertinent thought nudged at her again, stronger this time. Well, darn, she thought, it wouldn't require anything monumental of her. But he'd said a simple thank-you would be fine. And some people actually preferred to lead calm, boring lives.

She nodded. "Thank you very much." The man looked like he needed to be shaken and stirred. Resigned to the inevitable, she stood up on tiptoe, touched his stubborn chin with her fingertips and kissed Joshua Blackwell on his hard mouth.

She heard his swift intake of breath and the surprise rippling through him. It reminded her of a kid taking cough medicine. Just a little longer for the medicine to work, she thought, and felt his lips test hers. His hand wrapped around the back of her waist. Maddie wasn't sure if he was urging her closer to him or holding her steady. Either way, she melted a little.

She was surprised at his response. Even more surprised at her own.

Her heart hammering against her rib cage, she pulled back and took a deep breath. Slowly, she backed into the open door of her car. "Adventure in a dirt driveway," she murmured. "I've never been good at doing anything the simple way, but thank you. G'night," she managed to say, then tumbled into her seat.

Three

————

Joshua stood in the rain staring after her long after the sound of her bad muffler disappeared. He stood there in the dark, in the mud, in the rain.

Like a fool.

He snorted and trudged toward the house. From the way he'd reacted, one would think he'd never touched a woman, let alone been kissed by one. Swearing under his breath, he rolled his shoulders. His damp shirt clung miserably to his skin.

Maddie Palmer was trouble.

Although Joshua didn't possess a great deal of experience with women, he'd always believed he had well-developed instincts.

Maddie defied those instincts.

She was a flake with a good heart. A flirt with good intentions.

Underneath it all, though, Joshua sensed a strong inner core of strength, and he felt a connection with her. In a way, she was like him. She would do what had to be done. But he wondered how she managed the easy smiles if she was half as scared as he'd been when he'd begun raising his child alone.

He thought back to how she'd nearly knocked the stuffing out of him when she'd kissed him. She looked good, smelled good, tasted good, but she wrecked the natural order of things.

The woman was trouble.

When Maddie pulled into her driveway, it was around ten o'clock. Her stomach was growling and David was waking up. Bone weary, she removed him from his seat and made her way into her town house apartment. "Okay, sweet Pete, I bet you're going to want to eat and play a little. Just let me get a ham sandwich," she whispered. "It won't take me but a minute."

Setting him down in the portable folding crib, she zipped into the kitchen. No sooner had she slapped mustard on two slices of bread, than the doorbell rang and David began to whimper. She poked her head around the corner and saw her brother walk through the door.

"Where've you been?" Ben asked and snitched the partially made sandwich from her hand. "I stopped by two times. I was starting to wonder if something had happened to you." He took a bite and made a face, looking at the bread. "What is this, anyway?"

Still unaccustomed to her younger brother checking on her every night, Maddie shook her head. "Right now it's a mustard sandwich. It had the potential to be a ham sandwich if you'd waited, but it was destined for my mouth," she said, plucking the bread from his hands. "Not yours. Do you mind holding Davey for just a minute while I finish fixing this?"

Ben glanced over his shoulder and gave a half smile. "Okay. But if he tries to nurse my arm like he did a couple of days ago, he's all yours."

Maddie touched Ben's arm and forced a mock-solemn expression. "Life is fragile. Since you're David's godfather, if something happened to me, you'd have to deal with him sucking on you, spitting on you, etcetera," she said. "All the time."

Ben got a slightly queasy look on his face. "I know. Why do you think I'm so concerned about your well-being?"

"Why? Because you love and adore me," she told him, and gave him a quick kiss on the cheek.

"Oh, give me the kid. He's easier to deal with than you are," he grumbled.

Maddie smiled to herself as she turned to finish fixing the sandwich and pouring some decaf soda. Ben sat on the couch, telling David about women in a soft, gentle voice. Her tough brother with the shoulder-length light brown hair, single earring, meticulously developed scowl and Harley in her driveway was a sucker for her baby.

She scooted into the den and situated herself on the end of the sofa so she could eat and feed at the same time. Taking a quick sip, she stretched out her arms. "I can take him now."

Ben shrugged. "Go ahead and eat. We're having a man-to-man, and he's fine."

"Okay. Thanks." Knowing she was on borrowed time, she stuffed the rest of the sandwich down and started on the soda.

"You didn't tell me why you were out so late tonight," he prompted, and stood when the baby began to fuss.

"Ten o'clock is so late?"

"For you, it is. You haven't been out much past eight since my bud here made his appearance." David began to root against Ben's arm again. "Oh, no. None of that. Here he is,'' he said, then quickly turned her son over to her.

Maddie laughed and discreetly adjusted her top to nurse her baby. ''I took a meal to Joshua Blackwell and his son.''

He looked at her incredulously. ''You drove all the way past Catawba Mountain! In that disaster you call a car—''

''Maui,'' she said.

''And you didn't get lost?''

''I didn't say that. I got lost, but I eventually found his house. He and his son enjoyed the meal, and I left,'' she said. ''After Joshua changed my flat tire.'' *And I kissed him.* Her brother didn't need to know that little fact, especially since it was an action she wasn't likely to repeat.

''You're not really gonna take a meal over there every week for a year, are you? That's a little over the top even for you, Mad.''

''It is not. The man helped me when I needed it, and it meant a lot to me. I want to repay that in some way.'' *Even if it drives poor Joshua crazy?* She'd seen the expression on the man's face. She'd almost wondered when he was going to lift his fingers in a cross to ward her off.

''You get stubborn about the weirdest things,'' Ben told her.

Maddie glanced meaningfully at the python tattoo on her brother's forearm that had prevented him from getting several jobs. "I could say the same about you."

"That's different," he grumbled.

Maddie smiled. When Ben grew out of this rebel stage, he was going to be a great guy. She met his gaze affectionately. "Thanks for checking on me."

His brown eyes softened. "No problem. Call me if you need me."

"Have you talked to Mom lately?" she asked hopefully.

"The other day," he said. "Nothing new."

Maddie fought the stab of hurt. She knew what her brother was saying. Her mother still hadn't forgiven her for getting pregnant and having a baby when she was single. Maddie was beginning to wonder if her mother would ever accept David.

"Get some rest, Maddie," Ben told her.

She nodded. "G'night."

Within a moment the silence settled over her. Looking down at her son, she fought the sometimes overwhelming fear that accompanied the silence. He was so precious, she thought, marveling at him again. So incredibly precious, and she was totally and completely responsible for his health, safety and well-being. She caressed his fuzzy head and struggled with tears. Many times she wondered if she was up to the job. Not that she had any choice. She would fight tooth and nail anyone who tried to take David from her.

But still she wondered, and when she got tired of wondering, she resolved that she would be up to the task. She would learn to play baseball. Heaven help David, she thought, because she couldn't hit the broad side of a barn with a ball. She could in-line skate, though, and she could teach him to dance.

More important than all that, she wanted to be able to teach him to grow up happy and healthy. Believing in himself, able to give and receive, able to love and dream. Loneliness was powerful, but love and dreams were stronger.

Her mind switched to Joshua Blackwell and she frowned. He made her wonder. She'd originally thought he was a superstraight arrow. He either repressed his needs or didn't have any, she'd concluded. Maddie could hear her friend Jenna Jean fussing at her for jumping to conclusions.

She grimaced. Jenna might have been right this time. There was something unapologetically male, unforgivingly driven about Joshua. It had taken a few seconds, but he'd responded to her kiss. His mouth had begun to move in sensual exploration over hers. His chest had felt hard against her breasts. His thighs had glanced hers, making her aware of his strength and masculinity.

His response bothered her, but what bothered her most was her response. She hadn't expected her pulse to race, or her breath to shorten. She would never have predicted her knees would dip.

Well, she'd learned her lesson. Underneath that calm, stick-in-the-mud surface, was a mystery man with the potential of a powder keg. She wouldn't underestimate him again.

Joshua took a hot shower to eliminate the damp chill that permeated his bones after changing Maddie's tire. After a minute or two spent mentally assessing the day, he usually drifted off to a dreamless sleep. Tonight, however, sleep eluded him. When he closed his eyes, he was more aware of his body than he had been in years. His skin, his heart pumping, his breath.

He got up and swallowed a rare, double shot of whiskey, then returned to his bed. After a little while the alcohol and quiet took the edge off his tension, and he closed his eyes. When he finally began to relax, a vision of Maddie teased his mind like a buttercup under his chin. Trouble—the woman was trouble.

But she was so warm, so alive.

Joshua sighed and gradually drifted off to sleep. And he dreamed.

* * *

Maddie smiled at Patrick when he answered the door. "Beef Stroganoff okay?"

His eyes lit up. "Yes. Come in, Maddie." He looked past her to the car. "Where's Dav—"

Sweeping past him to the kitchen, she set down her baskets, then pushed aside her slicker to reveal the top of her sleeping son's head in the front pouch she wore. "I didn't want him to get wet." She glanced around. "Where's your dad? Is this a bad time?"

"He'll be back in a minute. One of the mares is giving him a fit."

She should seize this opportunity, she told herself, and leave. She didn't really want to see Joshua again, anyway. Especially after that little overture she'd intended as a charity kiss had ended up doing crazy things to her hormones. "I don't need to stay. I can just trade dishes next week and—"

Patrick looked horrified. "You're not gonna leave, are you?"

Uncertain, she hesitated. "Well, I just wanted to bring the food. Between getting lost, having to feed the baby, and your dad changing my flat tire, I think I put a crimp in your regular schedule last week."

"I would catch he—" Patrick stopped abruptly as if some inner voice reminded him not to swear in front of a woman. "Dad'll want to thank you for bringing it."

"And try to talk me out of bringing any more meals," she muttered under her breath.

Patrick chuckled. "Yeah, but you don't have to do what he says."

Spoken like a teenager yearning for independence, she thought. She opened her mouth to respond, but the front door whooshed open and Joshua stomped in with a string of curses that would have peeled the paint off the walls.

Maddie blinked, looking at Patrick. She tentatively peeked around the corner. His head drenched, water droplets dripping from his nose, Joshua was tearing off a gray rain slicker. His expression darker than a storm cloud, he must have felt her looking at him, because he lifted his gaze to meet hers. Maddie's heart jolted. He didn't look happy.

What are you doing here?

He didn't ask it aloud, but he might as well have.

His intensity rolled through her, surprising her. The image of a powder keg poked at her again. "Hi." She gave a limp smile. "I just dropped off the meal. Hope you enjoy it. I was on my way out."

She moved toward the door, but he shifted

slightly, blocking her way. "No need to rush," he murmured in his trust-me voice that reached under her skin. "There's a downpour right now."

"My windshield wipers work great," she said, and tried to edge past him. Unfortunately David took up a little more space than she estimated. She brushed against Joshua, then quickly stepped back.

"It'll be better if you wait. Have you eaten?"

Maddie hesitated, feeling trapped. "No, but I was going to—"

"Is there enough for three?"

"Not really," Maddie said.

"Plenty," Patrick called back.

Maddie frowned. No help from the son. She went for the direct approach. "You're probably not in the mood for company right now."

He lifted an eyebrow, then gave a quick exhale of amusement mixed with exasperation. "Oh, you mean because I'm about ready to shoot a prize-winning mare because she's turning up her nose at my stud?"

"Still kicking?" Patrick asked. "Are you sure she's in season?"

Joshua shot his son a dark look. "She's in season. She's just a picky, ornery female. Hell, I'm beginning to wonder if she needs violins and scented candles."

Maddie shook her head in confusion. "Excuse

me. I don't really know that much about horse farms. Don't you mainly just teach riding lessons and train horses?''

Patrick laughed.

Joshua almost smiled. He pulled off his boots. "This is a stud farm. We breed racehorses. I've got a triple-crown-winner stud. He's not young, but he can get the job done nicely. Owners bring the mares to me and I supervise the settling.''

"Settling,'' Maddie repeated.

"Breeding. Impregnation,'' he added when she looked confused. "Consummation.''

Maddie's eyes rounded. "Oh. So you're in the sex business.''

Patrick made a strangled sound of amusement.

Joshua blinked. He tilted his head to one side consideringly. "I can't say I ever thought of it that way, but, yeah, I guess so.'' His gaze flicked over her from head to toe. His eyes held curiosity and something else that made her slightly uneasy. "Take your coat off and stay awhile. I'll wash up.''

Maddie stared after him, then slanted a glance at Patrick. "Does he always give orders like that?''

Resignation warred with rebellion in gray eyes so like his father's. "Yep. And they usually get followed.''

Maddie tucked that bit of information away. A

strike against him, she told herself. Though she'd always been amused by arrogant men, she'd never been the least bit interested in getting involved with one.

Both Blackwell men encouraged her conversation during the meal. Maddie would almost swear Patrick was as hungry for feminine company as he was for food. He was an interesting kid, academically oriented, but he also enjoyed discussing music. Joshua didn't talk much, but she felt his gaze on her the entire time. It was just enough to keep her feeling disrupted.

They gave her privacy to feed David, then Joshua helped carry the dishes to her car. "The rain's almost stopped," he said. "Be careful. The lane might be slippery."

Maddie buckled Davey into his seat and slid his pacifier into his mouth. As she rose, Joshua stepped closer.

"I'm curious, Maddie," he said. "Do you kiss every man who changes a flat tire for you?"

Maddie tensed. "Well, to be perfectly honest, no man has ever changed a flat tire for me. I change them myself." She shrugged, wishing there was a teensy more space between them. "But it's true that I'm an affectionate person. I hug a lot, kiss on the cheek. I'm sure it makes some people uncomfortable. But you don't have to worry. I can tell you're not the touching type, so I won't be bothering you anymore by—'' She took a quick breath, blew her bangs and looked away. Why did she feel embarrassed? ''By kissing you.''

Joshua was silent a long, uncomfortable moment. If he would just move, she thought, then she could duck into her car and—

''Bother.'' He rolled the word around in his mouth as if he was trying the taste of it.

Maddie looked up at him. His gray gaze studied her.

He nodded slightly. ''Yeah, you bothered me when you kissed me. Did it bother you any?''

The hint of sexual challenge in his voice surprised her. She considered lying, but as in most things, Maddie always got caught when she lied. ''A little,'' she conceded reluctantly. ''But I didn't intend it that way. More as a thank-you and because I thought you hadn't been kissed in a while.''

Joshua stared at her. The corners of his mouth slowly inched up. ''That was a pity kiss?''

Maddie felt her face heat. Thankful for the cover of darkness, she silently swore. ''A thank-you,'' she muttered.

''A pity kiss,'' he corrected.

Damn. She sighed. ''It won't happen again.''

''Why not?''

She ducked under his arm and quickly shut the car door. "Because I don't think you need that kind of thank-you," she retorted, walking toward the other side.

"No more pity kisses for poor Joshua," he said, razzing her.

"No." Maddie pulled open the driver's side car door, but Joshua stopped it.

"That's a shame," he said. "Maddie," he prompted when she continued to stare at the car door and not look at him.

She reluctantly glanced up at him. "What?"

"Thanks for the meal." Then he closed the gap between them and pressed his mouth to hers.

There wasn't an ounce of pity in the gesture, Maddie thought, as her equilibrium went haywire. His mouth suggested and seduced, then he took her a step further when his tongue slid past the barrier of her lips and tasted her as if it was his right.

Her mind rebelled, but her body responded. She leaned into him, and her hands dropped to his arms, clinging to him. He wasn't rough. But she could taste his sensual curiosity and determination. His strength was tempered with gentleness. A potent combination, it got to her, slid past her defenses and took her breath. She could almost feel it knocking on her heart.

No.

That wouldn't do, Maddie thought. She couldn't open her heart to a man right now. She had to make a safe place inside and outside for her and her baby, and Maddie had learned that didn't include a man.

She pushed away from him and struggled for breath. "I believe that's enough gratitude from either of us," she managed to say. "No more thank-you kisses. No more pity kisses. No more," she said, and swallowed hard. *Wow.* "I'll see you next week. G'night."

Not waiting for his response, she got into her car and drove down the lane, mentally chanting, *No more.*

Four

Joshua stood in the rain staring after her long after the sound of her noisy, nearly dead muffler disappeared. He stared after her. Again.

He felt like a fool.

Again.

Joshua cursed and vowed that he was not going to get all worked up over a flighty woman like Maddie Palmer. He refused to attribute the dream he'd had last week to her, the first dream in over ten years. It was probably the food, he reasoned, as he stood in the rain. His stomach was unaccustomed to decent food, so his digestive system had kicked his brain into overdrive, and that was why he'd dreamed that night last week.

Logical explanation, he told himself, since he hadn't dreamed since then, and the dream hadn't been about Maddie. For Pete's sake, it had been about buttercups, a field of buttercups. Joshua resolved to dismiss her from his mind, the sensation of her lips from his, her scent from his nostrils.

No more, and no more it would be.

Turning away, he glanced down at the ground, and a beam from the porch light caught an object near his feet. He narrowed his eyes and shook his head, swearing again. The night wasn't over yet.

Maddie retraced her steps from her car for the third time as she jiggled David in her arms. She'd fed him again after she'd arrived home, then planned to put him down. A vital part of his go-to-sleep routine was missing, however. Every time she thought she had him jiggled to sleep and began to lay him down, he whimpered. The whimper grew to a frustrated cry that progressed to sobbing that made her feel like someone had ripped out her heart and stomped on it. She was going to join him with the sobbing soon.

Returning to the house, she shook her head again. She knew she should have bought another one. Feeling the lateness of the hour pull at her, she sighed and paced across her den, humming as she tried to soothe him. "Sleep, sweetie," she whispered. "You'll feel so much better." She swallowed her laughter. "I'll feel so much—"

A knock at the door caught her by surprise. Ben, she predicted, and opened the door. She blinked at the sight of Joshua Blackwell on her front porch. Dressed in worn jeans and a leather bomber jacket, he stood with his hair slightly mussed, his eyes fixed on her. Her heart did a quick climb into her throat.

"Hello?"

"Thought you might need this before morning." He raised his hand and offered her the missing pacifier.

"Oh, my goodness!" Maddie felt as if she'd just been given the Holy Grail. "Thank you!" she said, scooping up the pacifier. Maddie was so relieved she didn't know what to say. Of course, that didn't keep her from talking. "He must have spit it out, and then it fell out of the car. I can't tell you how grateful I am. He wasn't going down, and I was beginning to wonder if either of us would get any sleep tonight."

When Joshua continued to look at her without saying anything, she fought the dipping sensation in her stomach. "Well come in and—"

He shook his head. "Not necessary."

"Yes, it is," she insisted. "You've driven far to deliver a pacifier. Let me fix you a cup of coffee or cocoa before you get back on the road."

He started to shake his head again, and Maddie's impatience zoomed. "Do we need to argue about a cup of coffee?"

Joshua paused and gave a dry chuckle. "Guess not."

Feeling Joshua behind her, Maddie walked to the kitchen and turned on the coffeemaker. She shifted David to her other arm so she could wash the pacifier.

"Want me to take him?" Joshua offered.

She swerved to look at him. "Are you sure?"

"Yeah." He cracked an almost smile. "He doesn't look too heavy."

Maddie slowly handed David to Joshua. As weary as she was tonight, she felt a mixture of relief and apprehension at giving David to Joshua. It was partly anticipation of going back to work in a couple of weeks, she thought, when she would be sharing David's care even more. "Thank you," she murmured, noticing that Joshua held David naturally. He didn't appear the least bit awkward. His large hands held him against his chest, securely, but not too tight.

Strong yet gentle again. Her body remembered being held by him, and Maddie felt that insidious melting sensation inside her, surprising her again. She hadn't known she was vulnerable to the combination. After all, her fiancé had been a here-today, gone-tomorrow musician. She'd been the grounded one.

It was a strange sensation having a man besides her brother in her home. Here in her little self-proclaimed no-man's land, his unapologetic masculinity reminded her she was more than a mom. She was a woman.

She blinked away that thought. "You look like you've done that a time or two."

"Yeah, it's been a while. He's almost asleep."

Maddie washed the pacifier and rolled her eyes. "It's a trick. As soon as I put him down, he wakes up."

"Does the pacifier help any?" he asked, keeping his voice low. The sound was oddly intimate, and it echoed inside her.

She shook off the odd sensation. "It's magic. I wish everything about parenting were this easy. You have a problem? Go to the store and find something magic that costs under two dollars that will defuse any crisis."

"Scared?" he asked, surprise lacing the single word.

"Terrified," she said with a nod. "Does it show?"

He shook his head. "No. Not at all."

She took David from Joshua and her heart twisted as she looked at her sweet, trusting baby boy. "Well, I am," she whispered. "Scared spitless. Poor kid. He's got a mom who's hopeless in sports."

"Can you yell?"

She glanced at Joshua in confusion. "Yell? Yes, I can yell."

"Then you can cheer from the sidelines."

She smiled slowly, grateful this time. "Yes. I can do that." Coaxing the pacifier past his rosebud lips, she walked toward the upstairs nursery. "I have a few other—irregularities, though."

"Such as?" Joshua said from behind her.

Gently placing David in his crib, she lifted crossed fingers and counted to ten. "I think it worked," she whispered.

They walked down the steps together. "My long-time friend Jenna Jean who is an attorney puts it this way. I attract authority figures at unfortunate moments."

"Authority figures?"

"Traffic cops, meter maids and, just recently," Maddie added with a grimace, "the IRS."

Joshua winced too. "An audit."

Maddie nodded.

"Ouch."

"I've gone through different phases with this. I used to think it was bad luck. Then I decided it was timing that made the traffic cop give *me* a ticket instead of the guy who just passed me." She poured the coffee and gave him the mug. "I take responsibility for my little messes, but I do suspect there's some sort of karma at work here."

She thought about pouring herself a cup of coffee to do something with her hands, then remembered the caffeine and reconsidered. "I tend to bring disaster with me," she said.

"Uh-huh," he said, taking a sip and leaning his lean hip against her counter. "Bad luck. You're concerned you'll bring it on your kid, too."

Her heart tightened and she looked away. Maddie didn't want to think she'd bring bad luck to Davey, but sometimes when her defenses were down, she wondered.

"Or are you trying to warn me?"

She glanced up at him in surprise. "What?" Maddie wasn't sure she liked Joshua's knowing gray eyes. She supposed his being a stick-in-the-mud meant he wasn't easily fooled.

"Are you trying to warn me that you'll bring me bad luck?" he asked in a mild voice.

That hadn't been her intention. At least she thought it hadn't. "Why would I do that?" she asked, inhaling the combined scents of leather, coffee, and man.

"Because you got more than you bargained for with your pity kiss."

Maddie frowned. "Not that much more. It wasn't a big deal."

"Uh-huh," Joshua said, amusement mixing through his dry tone.

The sound was full of sensual challenge that she might have accepted another time. Maddie held his gaze, considering him. He didn't scare her, she told herself, though a shimmy ran down her nerve endings. As a rule, men didn't scare her. The exception being law enforcement officials. Men amused, irritated and charmed, but they didn't scare her.

It didn't matter, though, because now wasn't the time for a dalliance, even with a man like Joshua.

Now was the time for Maddie to get her act together for her baby and herself. She'd said *no more,* and perhaps subconsciously she was trying to reinforce it by talking about her bad luck.

"How has your luck been running since you met me?" she asked, winging it with his suggestion. "You were coerced into driving a pregnant woman on a motorcycle through the rain. You had to change a tire in the rain, and now you've delivered a pacifier, in the rain."

"Still trying to warn me off?" he asked with that sexy almost-smile on his face.

"You're a big boy," she told him with a little purr in her voice, unable to resist giving him back at least a little of his own. "I don't think I need to warn you about anything."

His gaze flicked over her, reminding her again, with shocking clarity, that she was more than a mom. "Yep," he said, taking a final sip of coffee, "and I won't be warning you either."

He brushed against her as he set the mug on the counter behind her. Maddie held her breath. He backed away and she exhaled.

He nodded. "See ya next week. Thanks for the coffee."

She followed him to the door. "Thanks for bringing the pacifier," she managed to say, wondering how he'd switched gears so neatly. "I'll be able to sleep now."

"Grateful?" Joshua asked, cocking his head to one side. "How grateful?"

Her heart slammed into third, another gear change. She could keep up, she told herself. She was just a little rusty. "I'll bring dessert next week."

His gaze slipped over her again, a quick, hot and forbidden caress, before his expression became bland. "I'll look forward to it."

* * *

Assistant District Attorney Jenna Jean Anderson had an unflinching blue gaze that inspired fear, discomfort, sometimes hostility, but ultimately truth. It wasn't just something she pulled out for courtroom drama. It was part of her personality, and had been since her early childhood.

"You will tell the truth, the whole truth and nothing but the truth," she said, clearly softening her husky voice, a direct contrast with her forceful personality. "But if you don't like that nasty formula your mommy gives you, make sure you burp on her, not your godmother."

She bent down and blew a raspberry on David's tummy. He smiled, and Jenna Jean grinned at Maddie. "Better tell the neighbors to lock up their daughters. He's going to slay the ladies."

"We're safe," Maddie replied. "You're prejudiced. You won't be able to prosecute him."

"He's adorable," Emily St. Clair Ramsey said as the three longtime friends shared lunch at her mother's well-appointed home. She squeezed closer to slide her finger under Davey's chubby chin. "He's got your eyes and mouth and—"

"If you say he's got my body, I'm dumping this mimosa on your head," Maddie warned, lifting her goblet of champagne and orange juice in a mock toast.

Emily gave a surreptitious flick of her blond

hair, but laughed. "What a joke. You're slimmer than before the pregnancy."

"Slimmer, not firmer," Maddie said glumly, then sighed. "It doesn't really matter, though, because I'm not going to date until David turns eighteen."

Jenna snorted. "And I'm Tinkerbell."

Maddie looked at her mimosa. "No. I've thought about this. I don't want to be one of those mothers bringing uncles in and out of their children's lives."

She sensed her friends' concerned gazes and looked up. "With Clyde, I could accept the way he was here today and gone tomorrow because it was just me. It was okay, most of the time," she added with a sad smile, "that he wasn't usually here when I needed him. It was okay for him to pursue his dream in New York and California. If I was lonely, a phone call would help. If it didn't, I could call one of you. But I can't be that way anymore. I've got someone besides me to think about now." She bit her lip. "I really don't want to screw this up."

Emily's eyes softened. "Oh, Maddie, don't be so hard on yourself. You're going to be fine. I'm sure you'll find a man who falls for both you and Davey."

"Spoken like a recently married woman who

has had her faith in the adult male gender fully restored,'' Maddie said, but couldn't contain a smile.

"I can't disagree with that,'' Jenna Jean said. "But I'm not sure a complete moratorium on dating is necessary.''

Both Emily and Maddie looked at Jenna in disbelief.

"How many dates have you been on lately?'' Emily asked mildly.

"I've been busy. Monster caseload—''

"You said that last year,'' Emily said.

"And the year before,'' Maddie added.

Jenna Jean quickly closed her mouth. "We weren't discussing me,'' she said in a semisnooty voice she used when she was trying to get past a sticky issue. "The point is, if a good man walks into your life right now, don't kick him out because of postpartum blues.''

An image of Joshua Blackwell flashed through Maddie's mind.

Jenna's eyes narrowed. "Who have you met?''

Maddie blinked. Was her face that transparent? Or was Jenna that intuitive? Perhaps a little of both. "Not really anyone.''

"Oh.'' Emily smiled slowly. "Then tell us about this 'not really anyone.'''

Maddie thought of Joshua and her stomach

turned a little flip. She took a sip of mimosa. "I haven't met that many new people lately except the man who helped deliver Davey."

Jenna perked up. "Oh, that's right. The rancher. What was his name? *J* something…"

"Joshua Blackwell. He runs a horse farm, a stud farm," she added, shaking her head.

Jenna snickered. "Stud farm? Bet there's a testosterone overload on that property."

Maddie couldn't disagree. "I take meals to his house once a week. I promised I would before he took me to the hospital on the back of his motorcycle."

Emily winced. "I still can't believe you did that."

"Better than having the baby on Highway 81," Maddie said.

"What's Joshua like?"

"He's the father of a teenage boy. Very responsible. Doesn't smile much. Very serious. Salt-of-the-earth type. Probably a stick-in-the-mud," she added, feeling as if she was stretching the truth.

"He doesn't sound like your type," Emily said, clearly disappointed.

"He's not," Maddie agreed, and squashed the little voice inside her that argued.

"Bet he's got a great body," Jenna said, looking

at Maddie as if she were going to poke the truth out of her.

"He does," Maddie conceded and paused. "He smells…" She hesitated, searching her mind for the proper description.

"Bad?" Emily wrinkled her nose.

Maddie shook her head. "No, not at all. He smells like leather and fresh hay and…"

"Horses," Jenna offered.

"Not really. I don't know what it is." She laughed. "It's a lot different than baby powder."

"Oh," Jenna said, the one word carrying a wealth of meaning. "Testosterone."

"It's all in the scent," Joshua told Maddie over dinner the following week. She'd brought spaghetti and meatballs, and he was enjoying her curiosity as much as the meal. Patrick had inhaled his meal and gone to his room to watch a show on MTV, and David was napping on a blanket, so Joshua had Maddie's undivided attention. He found he liked it.

He liked the way her brown eyes latched on to him and she cocked her head to the side while she listened. Her earrings dangled from her ears, and he flexed his fingers to restrain the urge to rub the shiny silver webs between his fingertips. He fought the same urge with her tousled auburn hair, glinting in the light. Maddie wasn't the only curious one. After the second dream he'd had last week, he was more curious about her than ever.

"The stud picks up the mare's scent and he's ready for action," he said, catching the faintest hint of a clean, spicy feminine fragrance that made him want to lean closer.

"You mean he just smells her and that's it?"

Joshua could tell that her nineties point of view was getting in the way of her understanding. "Not exactly all of it. Sometimes we have to let her get used to him, put him next to her for a day or so. We have to be careful, though, or he'll hurt himself trying to get to her."

Maddie shot him a doubtful look and sipped her tea. "Hurt himself? Isn't that a bit rash?"

Joshua wiped his hand over his mouth to hide a grin. "It's instinct. Pure, raw, animal instinct. When there's a mare around and she's in season, a stud's got one thing on his mind."

She seemed to consider that for a moment. "I guess I could say I've met some men like that."

He shook his head. The woman didn't have a clue, and for some reason he wasn't ready to admit he'd like to be the one to teach her. "Not like a stud. They paw the ground. They strut. I've seen one break through a fence, another kick through a barn wall. That's why we give them a long lead and watch them when they do the job."

Her eyes rounded. "You watch?"

"Sure. I'm getting paid to provide stud service, and it's my job to make sure no one gets hurt, including my stud. We tie the mare, but she can still do a lot of damage if she's skittish and kicks."

"You tie the mare," she echoed. "This is a lot different than I would have thought."

Voyeurism, bondage. He could practically see the images roll through her mind. She didn't look appalled, more surprised, and intrigued. His gaze dipped to the swell of her breasts beneath the scoop neck of her burnt orange blouse. He was close enough to see a few freckles on her chest. He was close enough to touch.

He wondered if she was just as curious in bed, then immediately smashed that thought. "It's not S&M, Maddie," he assured her. "We're just breeding tomorrow's triple crown winners the safest way we can," he told her.

She nodded. "That makes sense. You strike me as a man who would choose the safe way. I wouldn't think you would get caught taking a lot of chances."

"I've taken a few wild chances," he said, remembering the three times he'd banked on odds instead of reality. "I prefer a calculated risk."

She looked at him skeptically. "Oh, really. Tell me."

Not totally comfortable discussing this subject, he worked his shoulders and leaned back in his chair. "I guess you could call Patrick a wild chance. He was conceived in my daddy's '73 Chevy."

She smiled. "And do you feel like you won with that chance?"

"Yeah," he said with a nod. "The bad part was what happened to Gail. She lost some blood and they gave her a bad transfusion with hepatitis. It made her sick and she died of it four years later."

"I'm sorry," Maddie said, reaching her hand toward his arm. "I bet it was difficult."

He looked away for a moment, thinking what a sad time that had been in his life. "Yeah, it was." He sighed, ready to move on to another thought. "But there were a couple of other wild chances. I won my stud in a poker game."

"You?"

Joshua didn't know what to think of her disbelief. For some reason it chafed at him a little. "Yep. It was late. We'd had a little too much to drink, and this guy was determined to win. He didn't care about the money or the stakes. He just wanted the win. He liked high stakes, so he threw in his stud for the last turn of the cards. Everyone said he was nuts.''

He chuckled over the hand of fate. ''The cards were in my favor, and I've built my business on that win. The only other wild chance was buying this place. It was a mess, but that was more of a calculated risk. It had more to do with working long hours after the sun went down.''

She shook her head, still smiling. ''I don't know what to say. You just seem so solid, so dependable.''

He nodded and turned his hand over. ''Yep. You wanna finish reading my palm, Gypsy? You remind me of a gypsy.''

''Me?'' Maddie laughed. ''Okay. I'll do it no charge this time, but don't expect it again.'' Skimming her fingertips over his palm, she told him, ''You're careful.''

His gaze was caught by the gentle, rhythmic motion of her hand. It didn't make a damn bit of sense, but her fingers soothed something inside him at the same time they excited him.

How long had it been, he wondered, since a woman had touched him this way? He wondered how her fingers would feel on the rest of him, seeking and pleasuring. He wondered how her naked skin would feel beneath his hands. He wondered what kind of sounds she would make. He wondered...

"Determined. You're one to make things happen," she said. "And you're not the kind of man to spend a lot of time dreaming."

Joshua felt the punch of her assessment in his gut. Not the kind of man to spend a lot of time dreaming. He hadn't missed dreaming, he reminded himself. It had suited him just fine. He pulled his hand back and rubbed it against his thigh. "Right again. I'm not a dreamer."

Five

Maddie wondered why he'd pulled back so quickly. "I didn't mean no dreams at all," she told him. "That would be a little extreme."

"Not really," he said in a mild voice, but he seemed remote.

Puzzled, she frowned for a moment, then gave a half laugh to herself. "Maybe I should leave you one of my earrings tonight."

Joshua looked at her as if she had a screw loose. "Your earring?"

"Yeah, it's a miniature dream catcher. Good dreams pass through the center, and bad dreams are trapped in the web until they disappear."

"All that in an earring," he said wryly.

Maddie pulled her earring loose and dangled it toward him. "Need a little help with your dreams?"

"No."

His response was a shade too fast, she thought. Was it possible that Joshua had a weak spot? She studied him again. Not a pretty face, he had a tough jawline and mouth, and eyes that narrowed in doubt. The tough-looking mouth was deceptive, she remembered with a trace of discomfort. Nothing fanciful about this guy. On the outside he was all strength and hard angles. She'd thought he would be the same on the inside, but she was learning Joshua was far more complex.

"What were you like when you were a kid?"

He shrugged. "Like most kids."

She rolled her eyes. "Stingy answer," she muttered, and sighed. "I'll be more specific. What did you want to be when you grew up? What was your favorite penny candy? What was your favorite toy?"

He hesitated. "I wanted to be a professional baseball player. A pitcher. I played through high school and would have played in college, but Patrick came along and I took a different road. My favorite penny candy was fireballs, and," he said, nostalgic amusement gentling his rough features for just a second, "I had this plastic Godzilla monster that roared."

Ah, she thought, so he *had* dreamed. Maddie smiled. "We would have never gotten along as kids," she told, him and decided to "forget" her earring on the table. "I hated baseball. I wanted to be a rock star. I hid in my closet after I watched horror movies, and I would have fought you for the fireballs."

He cracked a grin. "So you were a troublemaker even as a child?"

Maddie shook her head and looked down her nose at him in a mock serious glance. "No. I've just always had unfortunate timing with authority figures."

"Uh-huh."

The sound of disbelief was sexy in an uncalculated way, and the thought of Joshua with dreams tugged hard at her heart. She understood about dreams that didn't come true.

Feeling a soft spot inside her form, she abruptly cut off her thoughts.

"I get caught," she told him and stood, flexing her resolve, and adding her next statement as much for herself as for him. "But not all the time." She was not going to get caught by any silly feelings for Joshua Blackwell.

* * *

That night Joshua avoided getting stuck in the rain staring after Maddie as she left. If he were a superstitious man, he'd think she brought the rain with her, because every time the woman came around it rained. Tonight, though, he didn't get wet, didn't change any tires, or find any pacifiers.

He didn't get kissed, either. That was okay, he told himself. He'd lived without Maddie's kisses for thirty-three years and he'd managed just fine.

He was pretty pleased with himself until he saw her earring on the kitchen table. Staring at it a moment, he picked it up and rubbed it between his fingers. The light reflected off the shiny silver, and he remembered the way the earring had bounced with each movement of her head.

She wanted to think of him as a dried-up old codger with no interest in the opposite sex. No interest in sex. That didn't sit well with Joshua. He shouldn't care, but he did. He was having a tough time resisting the urge to show her just how interested he could be.

He was having a tough time not putting his hands and mouth on her and learning what it took to change her perspective. She was a sensual woman, a feminine feast after a long fast. It was as if he'd forgotten to eat lunch, and it hadn't bothered him until Maddie called it to his attention.

She made him feel dissatisfied.

He pushed the sensation away, but the next morning when Joshua awoke, he immediately knew he hadn't dreamed. He felt oddly cheated.

"You did what?" Joshua demanded. The woman had gone way too far this time.

Maddie's eyes widened, and she held out her hands to Patrick for David. "I volunteered you to chaperon a dance at the community center."

"Why in hell did you—"

Maddie covered the baby's ears and frowned at Joshua. "Could you help me with something in the kitchen please?"

In a rotten mood, he tore off his raincoat. "I don't see why—"

"Ple-e-ease."

He inhaled deeply, his patience stretched. "Okay, but if you're concerned about me singeing your baby's ears, you might want to leave him with Patrick."

Maddie glanced at Patrick. "Do you mind?"

"Nuh-uh," he said, his expression one of relief that he didn't have to face his father.

"Thanks," she murmured, giving him a reassuring smile.

A premature reassuring smile, Joshua thought darkly, and led the way into the kitchen. He ignored the inviting aroma of beef stew and leaned against the counter. "Well?"

"While you were outside, Mrs. Quackenbush came to the door with her daughter and was selling tickets for the dance at the community center." She lowered her voice. "Have you seen Mrs. Quackenbush's daughter, Amy? She's very cute. She was looking at Patrick, and he was gawking at her, but was too shy to say anything, so..."

"So?" he said in a voice that sounded belligerent to his own ears.

Unfazed, she continued. "So, when Mrs. Quackenbush said they still needed some chaperons, I thought if you went it would give Patrick an opportunity to talk with Amy."

"It's a lousy idea."

She looked affronted. "It is not. It will only require a few hours of your time."

"How do you know I'm not busy that night?"

"I asked Patrick."

"I'm sure I've got something I need to do." If he didn't, he'd sure as hell find something.

"Oh, right," she said sarcastically. "You could always stay home, read the paper and watch the grass grow. This won't kill you."

"That's debatable," he muttered, his stomach growling along with his disposition.

Her eyes darkened with temper. "You know,"

she said, "the way you're acting, I'd almost think you're scared."

She was all dare, and he felt the kick of her challenge all the way down to his stomach. He resisted, barely, the urge to shut her tempting, impertinent mouth with a kiss. "I don't like other people making decisions about my schedule."

That took a little of the huff and puff out of her, he noted. She hesitated, then moved to the pot of stew and poured a bowl for him. "Well, you don't exactly have to go alone."

"Is that so?"

She was nervous for approximately thirty seconds before she grew impatient with herself.

Watching her toss the ladle into the pot, Joshua smothered a grin.

"Yes, it is," she said, and met his gaze with brown eyes that said "Don't mess with me." "I told Mrs. Quackenbush I would come with you."

Maddie considered herself a fairly tolerant individual. She knew she had a temper, but she tried to live by the philosophy that there was room for everyone and most everything if everyone made a little room.

Room for everything...except country music when it was performed by a group of musicians who hadn't quite mastered the concept of ''picking up the rhythm.''

She could accept its current broad-based appeal, but Maddie was a rock 'n' roll baby from way back. When she'd volunteered to help chaperon with Joshua, she'd had no idea she would be trapped listening to hours of country music and watching line dancing. It was cute and fun for the first thirty minutes. After that it began to wear.

The band started another twangy song with a tempo appropriate for the dead, and she longed for Bruce Springsteen as she and Joshua held up the back wall of the community center.

''You're twitching again,'' he said, next to her ear.

''I'm not twitching,'' she retorted, rolling her shoulder at the rush down her nerve endings. ''It's my body's natural response to a too-slow rhythm. Told you this was a lousy idea.''

''We're almost halfway through.''

''One-third of the way,'' he corrected. ''These things last at least three hours.''

Maddie did twitch then. ''Does the band ever take a break?''

''Maybe somebody will break some strings or something.''

She glanced at him and chuckled. ''It's like pulling teeth to get you to have a little fun, isn't it?''

He looked at her in mild disbelief. "Is that what we're supposed to be doing?"

"You know, Joshua, you look pretty good tonight, but you have a terrible attitude."

"I told you I don't like my schedule being decided for me."

"It wasn't decided. It just got a little assistance."

He paused a half beat, then glanced at the dance floor. "How good?"

Maddie blinked. When realization dawned, she couldn't keep from smiling. "You look very good," she told him. His Western-style white shirt showed the contrast of his dark complexion and drew the eye, particularly the female eye, to his broad shoulders. Add that to the way his black jeans emphasized his height and very nice backside, and Maddie suspected half the women in the room were secretly drooling.

"In fact, there are a couple of women on the other side of the room who haven't been able to take their eyes off you. Have you thought about asking someone to dance?"

"I don't think I need to up my torture quotient tonight."

Maddie sighed. "I'm curious. How long have you been so..." She searched for a nice term and couldn't find one. "Crabby?"

He looked momentarily disconcerted, then his face cleared and he glanced at his watch. "About an hour and fifteen minutes."

"No, no, no," she said, shaking her head. "I was thinking more in terms of years. And I wondered," she continued, "if it's related to a physical problem. You know like women have PMS?"

He wore that you-must-have-a-screw-loose expression on his face again and said, "PMS?"

"I've heard men experience something similar, but it doesn't necessarily have to be a monthly thing." She lowered her voice. "Prostate problems. I understand a backup can cause irritability."

He looked stunned. "And you think I have a back-up?"

"Well, Joshua," she said, and she truly wasn't trying to insult him. "You probably don't realize this, but you're cranky. When Mrs. Quackenbush brought the tickets, I thought it might be good for both you and Patrick. You, to get out among people instead of horses, and Patrick needs to get some exposure to girls in a social setting."

With a sinking sensation, she realized by his dark expression, he wasn't receiving her suggestion with an open mind. Oops. In over her head again. "But this backup thing is just a theory, and you might not—"

"Excuse me," a man said, interrupting her massive backpedaling effort. "Would you like to dance?"

Maddie smiled with relief. Saved by the bell, or in this case, a slightly older man who wanted to two-step. "Thank you. That sounds very nice. I'll be back in a few," she told Joshua, feeling his gaze on her as she accepted the other man's arm and moved to the dance floor.

Joshua stared at the red-haired madwoman as she chatted up Henry Krause and danced to the dragging tune played by the band.

Backup.

In his prostate, for God's sake.

He swore under his breath. If there wasn't a grain of truth to it, he'd be laughing himself silly right now. But he'd been thinking about Maddie a lot lately. In the barn, at the dinner table, in his bed. He still hadn't dreamed again, but he'd envisioned her in his bed, her arms wrapped around him, her body bare and susceptible, her mouth responsive. His thoughts had left him hot and hard, restless and wanting.

Joshua felt his crotch swell and swore again.

She wasn't beautiful, he tried to tell himself. She wasn't the most seductive woman on the face of the earth. She wasn't— Something inside him protested. She might not be the most beautiful or seductive woman, but she was the most interesting, vibrant, sexy-without-trying woman he'd met in his life. He wanted her. He knew he shouldn't do a damn thing about it.

He shouldn't, he reminded himself as the band finally took a break. Somebody didn't waste any time changing the tempo. John Cougar Mellencamp burst out loud and strong, singing "Hurts So Good." Joshua was still telling himself he shouldn't, when he watched in shock as his son asked Maddie to dance.

She nodded and laughed, swirling, twirling and singing along. The little skirt of her dress fluttered and flirted above her knees, grabbing his gaze, making him wish it would fly a little higher so he could see her thighs. Her hair bounced, swooping over her cheek, hiding one eye. Her shoulders shimmied making her breasts sway. She was just having fun, he told himself, but her abandon made him burn.

The song ended, and Joshua took a breath, expecting Maddie to return. But someone cranked up another rock 'n' roll number, and he watched a high school stud convince her to dance with him. Three songs later he was starting to feel impatient, restless…possessive. He snorted at the thought.

When a Tracy Chapman song oozed through the speakers, though, Joshua pushed away from the wall. It wasn't rational but he had given up on being rational at least for the moment. Making a path through the crowd, he caught her gaze, and she stared back at him.

"My turn," he told the hopeful high school kid, then turned to Maddie. "Dance with me." He took her hand in his, then put his other hand at her back and drew her closer.

"I didn't know you could," she said in a husky voice. "I thought it was against your policy to have fun."

He inhaled and drew in her spicy sweet scent. Her hair was soft under his chin. Her body was warm, and she moved in rhythm with him. "Maybe I need a little help."

"Having fun?"

Joshua kept his laughter to himself. His arousal, however, was another matter. "That'll do for a start."

Maddie shot him a questioning glance. "It'll do for a start?" Someone bumped against her, rubbing her body closer to his.

Joshua groaned.

Maddie was suddenly, completely aware of what kind of fun Joshua was referring to. After dancing with high school kids, it felt unbelievably good to be held by Joshua. His thighs brushed against hers, and with each movement she was conscious of his masculinity.

He was focused intently on her. She could see it in his eyes, feel it in the way he held her. His fingers laced through hers, while his other hand at her back kept her just close enough to mess up her breathing. A seductive trap. She deliberately took a deep breath. "So what tripped your trigger? Mellencamp or Prince?"

"Neither," he said, and rubbed his fingertips over her spine.

Maddie felt her breasts swell. She fought her response. "Joshua," she managed to say, "did you know you're looking at me like Sylvester looks at Tweety?"

A slow, predatory smile tilted his lips. "You make me hungry, Maddie."

His lower body slid against hers again, and she felt herself go warm and liquid inside. The man pulled her to both ends of the spectrum. He was so solid and dependable that she was lulled into believing she could relax with him, but at the same time he played havoc with her respiratory system.

She swallowed. "Hungry," she repeated. "That's why I bring you meals once a week." Lame, she heard in the back of her mind. Lame, lame, lame.

"Oh, lady." He rubbed his mouth over her bangs in a sweet, hot caress. "I'm not talking about food."

Six

"It's not me," Maddie whispered desperately, her heart pounding double time. "You've just been cut off from normal society so long that exposure to any woman would—" She swallowed. "Affect you."

He dipped his head. "Do you really think I'd react this way to Mrs. Quackenbush?" He asked the impertinent question in the same intimate voice that made her knees lose their stiffness.

Maddie paused. Mrs. Quackenbush appeared nearly twice Joshua's age and probably weighed the same as he did. "Okay, maybe not any woman, but—"

"You're right," he said, his gaze wrapping around her. "Not any woman. You."

Her heart stopped. She missed a step, and for once in her life, Maddie was speechless. She half wondered if he was going to kiss her right there on the dance floor, but he didn't. He just held her and looked at her and let his words sink in.

The song ended, and another teenager strutted up for a dance. Maddie clung to Joshua a few seconds longer before she realized what she was doing. She blinked, releasing him. "Thank you," she murmured to Joshua, and watched him walk to the back of the room. Still staring after him, she automatically began to move when the music started again.

She wasn't used to this kind of attention from a man. Her longtime pseudo fiancé had been fairly casual about his desire for Maddie. She had been more of a stabilizing force in his life than his great passion. His great passion had been his music, and though his absences had left her feeling lonely at times, she had adjusted.

Maddie had told herself she didn't need to be anyone's great passion. Enduring friendship, companionship and respect were more important. She felt a pang at the memory of Clyde. The last time he'd gone back to Los Angeles, he'd promised to bring back a ring next time. It had always been "next time." She missed him, but for some reason he'd never been around when she'd truly needed him, so she'd learned to get along without him.

Joshua didn't strike her as the kind of man to cut out when the going got tough. The notion that he wanted her, not just any woman, rocked her little no-man's land. She couldn't remember being wanted with that kind of intensity. It stole into her heart and roused all kinds of secret, foolish wishes.

Two hours later Maddie and Joshua left the dance.

"Where's Patrick?" she asked as they approached Joshua's truck.

"He's coming home late tonight. Going to a fast-food place with some friends." He opened the passenger door. "So it's just you and me since your brother is watching David."

Maddie climbed into the seat. "So it is," she murmured.

He entered from his side and headed for his house where Maddie had left her car. Acutely conscious of his closeness, she rolled down the window to create the illusion of space, even though it was early spring, and the temperature was a little cool.

"Too warm?" he asked.

"Not really. I like the breeze."

Silence. It seemed to wrap around them and bind

them closer together. Maddie couldn't stand it. "On a scale of one to ten, what would you say was the torture quotient for this evening?"

He glanced at her, then back at the road. "The evening's not over yet."

Her stomach dipped. "Then for the dance?"

He shrugged. "I give it a four with ten as the worst. I didn't have to dance with Mrs. Quackenbush, and Patrick finally got around to dancing with Amy."

Maddie nodded. "It took him a while, but when he finally got around to it, he didn't have any trouble."

"Bet you thought that since his father is a recluse—"

"I didn't call you a recluse," she protested.

"A social outcast," Joshua continued. "A modern-day monk—"

"I didn't say any of those."

"Nope," he said agreeably. "But you thought them."

She opened her mouth to protest, then hesitated and snapped it shut.

"I may be a recluse and a social outcast, but I'm no modern-day monk."

"I never said that," she repeated. "To be perfectly honest, I never even thought that one."

"Okay. What words did you choose?"

Maddie looked out the window and grimaced. How did she get herself in these predicaments? She went with his positive attributes and hoped that would be enough. "Solid, dependable, serious."

"And?"

She grimaced again. "Cranky and a stick-in-the-mud," she muttered in a low voice.

He gave a rough chuckle as he pulled into his drive. "Can't be all bad. It made you give me a pity kiss."

She felt her cheeks heat. "I thought we'd already discussed this." She frowned when she noticed he drove past the house. "Where are you going?"

"To the top of a hill. You'll like it. It's a clear night, and you can see the stars."

He wound around on a curvy dirt road, then pulled to a stop at the top of a hill. "C'mon out," he urged, and was at her door within seconds.

"Nice manners," she said as he helped her. "How did that happen?"

"Automatic response. My father isn't the most educated man, but he demanded respect and politeness from his kids."

"You see him much now?"

"Nope. I was the oldest and was offered a baseball scholarship to college, but since Patrick came I couldn't go. They were disappointed and then disappointed again when I moved here from Kentucky.''

Maddie sighed, feeling a connection with him. ''Disappointment's hard to live with sometimes.''

''Yeah. I guess I was always too busy to worry about it much. It bothered me until I realized that maybe we both let each other down. I didn't do what they wanted. They weren't there for me when I needed them.''

She looked at him in surprise. ''That's pretty impressive.''

He gave a half smile. ''For a stick-in-the-mud social outcast?''

''Yes. My mother's not speaking to me right now. She thinks I should have given David up for adoption.'' She breathed in the cool air and looked at the stars. They looked like a million diamonds on a blue-black blanket.

''Has she seen him?''

''Pictures. My brother showed her some pictures.''

''Her loss.''

Maddie shook her head. ''Everyone loses in this situation.''

''Yeah, but she loses more. She doesn't get to hold her grandson, and,'' he said, moving closer to her, ''she's missing out on you.''

''I hadn't thought of it that way.''

"Nope. You're too busy feeling ashamed."

She shook her head in surprise again. "For a humorless social outcast, you sure know a lot."

"Oh. We've added humorless."

She covered her mouth. "Oops. Who said that?"

"You're cold," he said, noticing her slight shudder. "Time to get back in the car."

Reluctant to leave, but growing cooler, she returned to her seat. "If I lived someplace like this, I'd probably climb this hill every night to look at the stars."

"Not when it rains."

"But I bet it's pretty when it snows," she told him, and craned her neck to look out the front window. "It's so quiet, peaceful."

"It is."

The deep tone of his voice got under her skin. Looking at Joshua, Maddie sighed and leaned back in her seat. "Thank you for bringing me here."

He cocked his head to one side, studying her, and his mouth tilted with a hint of a grin. "No thank-you gestures?"

Maddie's heart tightened at the dangerous expression on his face. "You mean kisses?"

"Uh-huh." He leaned closer.

It was amazing how sexy he could make uh-huh sound. She smiled because nothing was going to happen. She was certain. "Joshua, you're not the kind to be kissing women in your car."

"Is that so?" He lifted his hand to her hair.

Her confidence dipped a little. "Yes, it's so. You're practical and dependable and—"

"And I want you."

Maddie's breath stopped. "Somebody must have spiked the punch," she said breathlessly. "How much did you drink, anyway?"

Joshua shook his head and leaned still closer. "This isn't whiskey talk, Maddie. It's me, and you're wrong. I am the kind to be kissing you in my car."

She was all set to point out that she'd said *women* in a general sense, not specific, but his mouth covered hers. She felt his fingers slide beneath her hair to the nape of her neck.

Warm and inviting, he swept the tip of his tongue over the seam of her lips. Her stomach fluttered at the gentle pressure. She inhaled his scent and felt dizzy. It was so easy to respond, to rub her lips against his and learn the taste and texture of his mouth. When he gave a nearly inaudible groan, it was so easy to open her lips and test his tongue with hers.

He continued his gentle, sensual massage on her neck, but his mouth grew more avid, and suddenly the temperature in the truck jumped several degrees. Leaning into him, Maddie opened her mouth wider to accommodate his probing tongue.

Reeling from the sensation of falling, Maddie braced her hand on his chest. The kiss went on and on until Joshua pulled back, slightly, to take a breath.

His eyes burned with desire, and he shook his head. "Lady, you are something else."

He lifted his fingers to her lips, and she closed her lips around one. He closed his eyes briefly as if in pain, then opened them and watched as she took his index finger inside her mouth.

It wouldn't go too far in a car, she told herself. Maddie suckled his finger, not wanting to stop.

He swore. His gaze fell over her, lingering on her lips and throat, then her breasts.

He hadn't touched them, but Maddie felt her nipples tighten. She would almost swear there was an electric current humming in the air. A bare electrical wire too close for safety.

It sent off a warning bell in her system, but Joshua leaned close again, and all she could hear was the thumping of her heart. He pressed his open mouth against hers, rolling it from side to side, more sensual tease than kiss.

He made her want more.

He slid his finger down her throat to the top of her breasts, skimming his finger back and forth.

"Every man at that dance," he said against her mouth, "was wondering what was under this little dress."

Feeling as if she were turning to liquid, Maddie swallowed. "Just the regular things. Bra and under—"

He gently bit her lip, and she sucked in a quick breath. He kept up the maddening skimming of his finger across the tops of her breasts. A restless sensation flicked at her nerve endings. She wanted him to touch her.

Closer, he moved his finger and lured her tongue into his mouth. Closer again, and she arched toward him. *Touch me. Touch me.*

His finger dipped beneath the satin cup of her bra and glanced her swollen nipple. A little moan bubbled up from her throat. The sound must have shredded another layer of his control. He stopped playing with her tongue and took her mouth in earnest. Within seconds her back zipper was released and the bodice of her dress was pushed down.

He rubbed the tight, sensitive tip of her breast between his thumb and forefinger, and she felt a corresponding thrumming in her womb. She moaned again, clutching at his shoulders and kissing him back with equal intensity. She felt his heat beneath her fingers, sensed the deep, needy thud of arousal pounding through him.

Everything he was doing, every move he made, tightened the tension inside her, and Maddie was so aroused she was spinning from it.

Pulling his mouth from hers, he took another breath. His eyes reminded her of the sky during an electrical storm. "I want to touch you," he told her. "Everywhere." He pushed the cups of her bra down and looked at her bare breasts. "You're so beautiful."

He cupped her, still taunting the tips with his thumbs.

Maddie pushed against him, needing to quell the ache. He gently squeezed, then lowered his head and took her into his mouth.

The sensation was so erotic she closed her eyes. For the last year her body had been devoted to growing and nurturing a baby. Joshua reminded her she was a woman, with needs, the need to touch and be touched, the need to want and be wanted.

His features softened by moonlight, he suckled her nipple, and the ache inside her grew worse instead of better. "Ohhhh," she moaned.

Tugging at his shirt, she fumbled but managed to loosen his buttons. She ran her hands over his chest, her fingers luxuriating in his defined muscles and silky hair.

He made a rough sound of pleasure, then lifted his head. "This isn't enough." He pushed the seat back and pulled her onto his lap, then slid his hands up her thighs to where she was damp and needy. Through the panty hose, he rubbed her, making her wetter, making her ache more.

Restless, Maddie shifted in his lap, feeling his hardness against her hip. She wanted to touch him there where he was swollen with wanting her. She wanted to bring him the pleasure of her hand. She wanted…him.

She made a sound of frustration, and he squeezed her thigh.

"What is it?"

"I want— I need—" She closed her eyes. "Ohhhh!"

"I hate panty hose," he told her. "You've got too many clothes on."

Maddie tried to sit still, to make the havoc in her mind quiet. She tried to make the car stop spinning. "I'm wearing less than you at the moment."

He was all concern, closing his arms around her. "Are you cold?"

"Not exactly," she managed to say, feeling as if her skin was on fire. "Joshua, we are in a truck." She couldn't believe it.

"Yep. It's a little restricted for what I want to do with you."

He pulled her against his chest and nuzzled her hair. The gesture should have helped to calm her, but Maddie felt like a whirling dervish on the inside. Edgy, rattled, needy. She wanted to be with him in every sense of the word. Intimate with him.

She bit her lip. "I thought we said we weren't going to do this anymore."

"You said that. I didn't."

She was going to scream if she didn't get some air. Sitting up, she pulled up her bra and dress. "Can you zip me, please?" It was the least he could do since he'd unzipped her.

Joshua frowned. "Yeah, but—"

Maddie made a strangled sound of frustration. "Please?"

"Okay, okay." He zipped her, then eyed her warily as she scooted to her seat and pushed open the door. "What's with you?"

"Have you ever heard the expression 'Hotter than a naked jalapeño pepper in June'?"

"Can't say that I have."

"Well, I feel like that jalepeño pepper right now!" Maddie jumped to the ground, slammed the door behind her and fanned her face.

Joshua watched her in amazement. She looked as out of control as he felt. For Pete's sake, he'd wanted to devour the woman. He'd mentally done an inventory of his feed supplies to keep from tearing through her nylons and begging her to let him in. He was still hard, still wanted her.

He had known he'd wanted her, but he'd had no clue how responsive she would be. He'd had no idea how her husky moan would feel like an intimate stroke. He'd had no idea she could possibly want him half as much as he wanted her.

Swearing, he breathed in deeply. His body felt tight, primed. For Maddie. Based on her little stroll in the cool night air, his body was not going to get what it wanted.

He squeezed the bridge of his nose. Hell, he was going to have to figure this out, but now was not the time. Right now, he had the brain power of a stud rearing to go. Which was zero.

He sighed and pushed open the car door to join her outside. The night air hit him like a slap. "Who needs a cold shower after this?"

Maddie pressed her lips together and gave a weak smile, but she didn't look at him. Her arms were crossed over her chest.

"Cat got your tongue?"

"No, you did."

His body responded immediately to the thought of her mouth, despite the cool temperature. "And

I'd like it again," he said, and put his arm behind her on the side of the truck.

Maddie gave a soft groan and looked up at the stars. "I'm embarrassed."

He jerked his head to stare at her. "Why?"

"Because I lost it, just lost it. I was practically jumping you in your truck."

"I wish," he muttered, then shook his head. "I think you're confused."

"I won't argue with that."

"You weren't jumping me. I was jumping you."

She looked at him skeptically. "You look calmer than I feel."

"I have to. If I showed you how much I want you, I'm afraid it might scare you."

Her eyes widened, and she stared at him. "I've never been that out of control before. I don't think I like it."

"I did," he said without missing a beat.

She gave a shaky laugh, and the sound of it squeezed his heart. He took her chin in his hand and lowered his head. "Maddie, anytime you feel like losing control or jumping me, go right ahead."

Seven

"**B**ottle? What happened to—" Joshua's gaze dipped to her breasts as she sat on his sofa, and Maddie was struck with the memory of how he'd touched her last week.

"I switched to formula when I went back to work. No problem, for you, Studmuffin, huh? You just want your food," she said to Davey, and watched him smile around the bottle nipple. She sighed. "He's so gorgeous. He'll have to beat the girls off with a stick."

"Are you sure it won't be you beating the girls off with a stick?" Joshua asked with a lifted brow.

"Not if they're nice," she said sweetly.

Patrick patted Major, then walked up beside Joshua and crossed his arms over his chest. "He's not bad for a baby. He doesn't scream that much or anything."

Maddie chuckled. "Thanks. I wish I could take credit for his temperament, but I think it's most likely related to a mature digestive system."

"Oh, yeah?"

"That means he burps after she feeds him," Joshua said.

Patrick shrugged, and Maddie expected he might return to his room as he often did after dinner, but he stayed.

"Would you like to feed him?" she asked.

Patrick's face shifted to wariness. "I—uh—well—"

"You don't have to. I didn't know if you'd ever held and fed a baby before."

He shrugged again, his standard gesture. "Okay."

"Why don't you sit down beside me?" Maddie asked, and positioned David in Patrick's arms. "It probably won't take long. He's like a little Hoover." She patted David and smiled at Patrick. "You look like you've been doing this for years."

"He's fed some colts on occasion," Joshua said.

"That must be it." She noticed Patrick kept

glancing at her, then looking away, as if he wanted to say something. She took a stab at what might be on his mind. "Have you talked to Amy since the dance?"

He nodded. "She talks to me at school."

Maddie nodded. "Do you say anything back?"

"Yeah," he said, then added, "when I can think of something."

Maddie lifted her eyebrows. "Does she make you a little nervous?"

"A little," he conceded, glancing quickly at his father. Fidgeting slightly, he cleared his throat. "When you were in high school, how did guys get you to go out with them?"

Maddie saw how much the question had cost him, and her heart went out to him. It made her chest tighten to think David might be asking her the same kind of question someday. "Well, they called me on the phone. They walked me to class and ate lunch with me. They asked me questions."

"What kind of questions?"

"Oh, what kind of music I liked, what movies I'd seen, what TV shows I watched. Those kind of things."

"I think he's done," Patrick said, since the bottle was empty and David was half-asleep.

"I think you're right." She lifted Davey to her shoulder and gently rubbed his back.

"Did it work?"

Confused, she looked at Patrick. "Did what work?"

"Asking questions and calling you on the phone. Did that make you go out with the guy?"

"Sometimes," she said. "It also depended on whether or not I thought he was cute."

"Oh," he said, his expression saying he didn't think he fell into the cute category. "Did flowers help?"

"Flowers always help, and they don't have to be roses," she told him, but didn't reveal the fact that she had never received flowers from a man. "Little presents help."

"Little?" Patrick's voice cracked in concern.

"Very little," she assured him. "A cassette of a favorite musical group. A key chain with my initial." Maddie was naming the gifts she would have liked to receive, but hadn't. She remembered again how Clyde had always been broke, and she smiled. "What works even more, though, is to listen to her. If you learn to listen well enough, you'll find out what she likes."

"Most women are more obscure than that," Joshua said cynically.

"Listening is a difficult skill for some men to master," she said right back at him.

"Tell her she's pretty. Tell her you like her hair,

the way she smells and the way she smiles,'' Joshua said.

"That worked for you?" Patrick asked.

"Like a charm."

"But if it's a line," Maddie warned, not completely certain which Blackwell she was instructing, "then she may eventually find out, and she'll dump you. It needs to be the truth." She paused. "Tell her how she makes you feel."

"Like I'm gonna throw up?"

Joshua laughed and tossed Maddie a you-asked-for-it glance.

"Your good feelings," she said, looking down her nose at Joshua. "But that's after you go out with her. When you get to know her better, you might change your mind. That's what dating is for."

Patrick nodded. "Yeah, but where do I take her?"

"First date is ice cream," Joshua said. "Cheap and fast. You can't screw up ice cream."

Unable to resist some gentle ribbing, Maddie looked at him in amusement. "I'm surprised you remember back that far."

He gave her a swift glance full of heat and challenge. "Like riding a bike. You never forget."

Maddie felt her heart trip. Joshua reminded her of a bear who'd been hibernating. She'd mistaken him for half-dead, but now he was waking up. And he was hungry for her. She just wasn't sure what would be left of her if he consumed her.

She turned her attention back to Patrick. He was much safer. "This is going to sound hokey, but you would be surprised how much thoughtfulness and good manners will work."

Patrick looked as if he was processing all the information he'd received. "Did you dump many guys?"

"Enough," Maddie said wryly. "I think I attracted a lot of jerks back then." She laughed in memory. "There were some I should have dumped sooner than I did."

"Okay," Patrick said, and stood. "Thanks."

He started to leave the room, then turned around, a thoughtful expression on his face. "What was the best thing any guy ever gave you?"

"Besides David?" she asked, savoring the soft weight of her baby. She heard Joshua's swift intake of breath and knew what he must be thinking. "But you need to remember I'm twenty-seven, out of high school, and I would much prefer sharing the responsibility of raising a child."

"Yeah, I know all about condoms."

"Yeah, well they can break," she muttered under her breath. "Two kinds of birth control are better than one, but you already know that. And

I'm sure you already know it's more than bodies that are involved when people have sex, so you need to save it.'' She shot Joshua a quick glance and sensed his approval.

She smiled at Patrick. "My favorite gift from a guy was a song he wrote for me." She shook her head and sighed. "I've always been a sucker for a guy with a guitar."

A few minutes later Joshua walked with her out to her car. The earlier rain had cleared, and the night air was once again cool. As soon as she tucked David into his car seat and closed the car door, Joshua pressed his chest and lower body against hers, gently trapping her against the car.

She told herself to ignore the way her heart jumped in her chest. "It might be kinda hard for me to get in and drive home."

"You in a rush?" he asked, lowering his mouth to nuzzle her ear.

Maddie shuddered. "Not really. Just don't want to wear out my welcome."

He skimmed his lips over her neck. "No chance."

She tried to stifle a whimper, but didn't completely succeed.

He gave a low growl. "I love the little sounds you make. It makes me wonder how you'd sound in bed."

A wicked, illicit thrill raced through her, but she was torn. "I don't know if that means I should shut up or not."

"Not," he told her. "Have I told you how pretty you are?"

Maddie melted, even though she knew it wasn't true.

He wove his fingers through her hair. "And I like your hair, the color, the way it feels, the way it moves."

Maddie closed her eyes. His hands felt good. His words felt wonderful. "Oh, Joshua."

He nuzzled her again. "I love the way you smell."

"Baby powder."

"It smells sexy on you."

She opened her eyes and laughed lightly. "You're crazy."

"Maybe." He lifted his finger to her lips. "I like the way you smile."

Not certain whether to laugh or cry, Maddie shook her head. "Very good, Joshua. Very good." She pushed hard at his chest and walked around to the driver's side of the car.

"What?" he demanded, following after her. "What?"

"Nice lines," she said. "They almost work like a charm."

"Aw, hell, Maddie, you knew I meant them."

"Well, here's one for you," she tossed back at him as she swung into her seat. "You make me feel like throwing up."

Joshua checked the window one more time and frowned.

"You don't see her?"

"No." This was the first Wednesday Maddie hadn't shown up with a meal in weeks and weeks. Although Joshua enjoyed her food, he wasn't nearly as concerned about the meal as he was about Maddie.

"You think we should call?" Patrick asked, revealing that he'd grown accustomed to her visits, too.

"Just a few more minutes," Joshua said, though his instinct was to go out looking for her. What if she'd found her way into his crazy neighbor's yard again, and this time the guy had decided to use his shotgun?

He heard a loud roar down his lane and felt a sliver of relief. That was Maddie's muffler. Major pawed at the door.

Patrick glanced at him and nodded. They both went to the door, ready to run down the steps to help her.

Maddie's car door opened, and a man got out

with a pizza box. He ran up to the porch. His hair was long, he wore one tiny golden hoop earring, and he was dressed in jeans and a biker T-shirt. "Hey, I'm Ben, Maddie's brother. She can't come tonight. The baby's sick, so she asked me to bring you pizza. You're Joshua, right?"

Joshua nodded, seeing nothing of Maddie in the man until he looked into Ben's eyes. Same brown, same vitality. "Come in out of the rain and join us."

Ben hesitated a moment, then made a face at her car and shrugged. "Thanks. I think I will. There's two pizzas. Maddie told me to choose, so there's one super supreme and one pepperoni."

"You did good," Joshua said as they moved toward the kitchen. "Patrick will probably chew through the box."

"Da-ad," Patrick said in disgust, still surreptitiously staring at Ben.

Joshua grabbed some cans of soda from the refrigerator. "Bachelor china tonight, Patrick," he said.

Patrick pulled out paper plates and napkins, and Ben grinned in approval. "You mean there's another kind?"

"What's wrong with David?"

Ben shook his head. "Ear infection. She took

him to the doctor and got some medicine, but he'll probably be screaming again tonight, poor kid.''

Joshua winced. "Again?"

"Yep. She stayed up last night. I'd give her a break tonight, but I'm working the late shift at Tony's Bar." Ben took a bite of pizza and washed it down with soda. "She looks like hell."

An idea nudged at Joshua, and he let it ferment in his mind while he led the conversation in a different direction. "I don't know much about you, except you're the godfather," Joshua said, "and you were initially told Maddie had delivered quintuplets."

Ben chuckled darkly. "That's our Maddie. Keeps us all on our toes." He gave Joshua an assessing glance. "I've gotten an earful about you."

Surprised, Joshua paused mid-bite. He swallowed. "Is that so?"

"Yep, she told me all about you and your son. Said Patrick was real bright. Great kid."

Patrick sat up straighter. "She did?" His voice broke, and he cleared his throat. "She did?" he repeated in a deeper tone.

"Yeah. And she's determined to stick out this meal thing even if it kills her."

A sliver of guilt stung him, and Joshua bit back an oath. "I've tried to get her to stop. It's not necessary."

"Forget it," Ben said. "She's made up her mind. She says you were there when she needed somebody and she won't forget it." Ben paused and flicked a mushroom off his pizza. "That's a new experience for Maddie, especially with a man. My dad traveled a lot when we were growing up, so he wasn't around much. And Clyde," Ben said in disgust, "was never around. That guy was more of a flake than Maddie. Talented, but he didn't deserve her."

He glanced at Joshua again, as if he were assessing him. "There's more to Maddie than meets the eye," he said in a soft, but firm voice.

Joshua took a second look at Ben again. He heard a subtle warning in his voice. The brother looking out for his sister. With the way Joshua felt about Maddie, perhaps someone should be looking out for her.

Late that night Joshua was restless and unable to sleep. He prowled through the den and kitchen, drank a glass of milk and ate a packaged cookie. Making a face as he ate the dry, tasteless cookie, he realized this was probably one of the reasons why he'd never gotten fat. His cooking sure wasn't anything to brag about, and he'd never possessed the knack for finding the good stuff at the grocery store. If he ate Maddie's cooking on a more regular basis, he'd bet he would be breaking the scale.

Joshua frowned. He had grown accustomed to seeing her once a week. He looked forward to it, sometimes even felt impatient about it. Feeling the burn of hunger inside him, he suspected the sensation had nothing to do with food and everything to do with Maddie.

He would like to think it was just sex, but something about Mad Maddie got under his skin and grabbed his heart. He wondered if she was walking the floor with David tonight. He remembered the loneliness of being the sole person responsible for a small child, and the idea of her fighting off the exhaustion during another long night nagged at him.

He rolled his shoulders and tried to dismiss the image, but it nagged and pulled and tugged. The same idea that had struck him during dinner nudged at him again.

"A crazy idea," he muttered, glancing at the kitchen clock which read 11:30 p.m. "Crazy."

Walking back to his room, he shoved on jeans, a shirt, socks and shoes, all the while muttering about "his freakin' crazy idea." He woke Patrick long enough to tell him where he would be, then took off in his truck.

With no traffic, he made the trip in thirty-five

minutes. He was just going to check on her, he told himself, planning to keep his craziness to himself. If her town house was dark, he would turn around and go back home without even knocking on her door.

There was, however, a light.

He tapped lightly and waited, then tapped again. This was nuts, he thought, and was just turning to leave when the door opened.

With David propped on her shoulder and sucking his pacifier like there was no tomorrow, Maddie stared at Joshua for a full unblinking moment. He saw the wear and tear of the past twenty-four hours on her face. Shadows under her eyes, tousled hair, she wore a Betty Boop nightshirt. The sight of her self-consciously rubbing her damp cheeks and ducking her head turned him inside out. She was a mess, and he couldn't remember when a woman had affected him more.

"I heard you were having a rough night."

She nodded and sniffed. "You sure you want to join our sobfest?"

He bit back a grin and shrugged. "I didn't have anything better to do."

Maddie groaned in misery. "What about sleep?"

Already tried and couldn't, he thought wryly. "You gonna let me in?"

"Oh, sorry," she said as if the idea hadn't occurred to her. She stepped aside. "I wasn't expecting you."

"Or anyone else after midnight," Joshua murmured, and followed her into the den.

"Midnight?" She squinted her eyes at a porce-
lain clock on the fireplace mantel as she paced. "I
hadn't noticed. Do you want coffee or milk or—"

"I want you to sit down," Joshua said, wondering if she was going to faint from exhaustion.
He had the strongest urge to pick her up and carry
her to bed, but he suspected she would protest.

Maddie glanced at him and shook her head. "No
can do. Studmuffin here has got a killer earache,
and walking him is his only relief. I can't bear to
hear him cry anymore."

"Medicine?"

She continued to pace. "Yep. The doctor said it
should kick in within twenty-four to forty-eight
hours."

"You haven't asked why I came," Joshua said.

"No." Maddie gave a light laugh. "I guess I'm
getting a little punchy."

"Ben said you had a rough night last night,
too."

She nodded and focused on the pattern of her
carpet.

"I remember how staying up with Patrick was rough sometimes. Makes for a helluva long night."

She nodded again.

"So I thought I'd take over for a while."

Maddie nodded yet again, continuing to pace.

Her lack of responsiveness made him uneasy. "Maddie, did you hear what I said?"

She looked up at him and blinked. "Gosh, I wish the room would stop moving."

For Pete's sake, the woman was practically swooning. He extended his arms. "Give me the little one, babe."

She frowned as if trying to understand. "Pardon?"

"I said, give me David, and you go to bed."

She closed her eyes. "No. Geez, I wish my equilibrium would get its act together. Don't worry. David'll settle down in a little while and—"

"You'll fall flat on your face if you don't get some sleep," Joshua said firmly. He gave a little flick of his fingers. "Give him to me."

Her gaze met his, and he could see that he had penetrated the thick fog of her weariness. He sensed she was finally seeing him for the first time this evening. A mixture of emotions played across her face. He watched her let go of her defenses just a little. Relief and trust smoothed her features. She trusted him. It was odd as hell, but her trust made him feel taller, stronger.

Even odder was the fact that underneath her weariness and all the other emotions, he knew she wanted him. It was more than a physical want, though it included desire. She wanted him for the man he was, inside and out. The wanting laid bare in her eyes rocked him.

"Just for an hour," she said, and handed David over to him, patting her baby and making sure his pacifier was secure. "Any longer wouldn't be fair. I'm not sure this is."

She looked at Joshua again and shook her head, gratitude shining in her brown gaze. "You're an amazing man," she whispered, then rose on tiptoe and lightly kissed him. "Amazing. All I need is an hour. Wake me in an hour. Okay?"

"Sure."

Maddie awoke when the first sliver of sunlight peeked through the crack in her curtains. She lay still for a moment, sensing something wasn't quite right. She glanced quickly at David's bassinet and found it empty. The light dawned in more ways than one. She remembered Joshua and winced. He'd stayed all night. He must be exhausted.

Pushing off the covers, she scrambled downstairs and stopped dead at the entrance to her den. Joshua sat in the rocking chair, his feet spread apart on the floor, his large hands holding David securely against his chest and his head tipped forward.

David was sleeping. So was Joshua.

A rush of emotion squeezed her heart like a vice. Maddie took a deep breath. It almost hurt to look. To see a man hold David with such tenderness and care was the stuff of her dreams. She wanted David to have everything he needed, and as much as she tried, she could never be Daddy too. She'd just assumed she would have to go it alone, and though she knew Joshua wasn't in the market for a baby son, it was tempting to play with the magical thought for a moment.

What if Joshua fell in love with her and her baby and wanted to keep them both? What if...

Maddie shook herself and sighed. *Get a grip.* She couldn't blame herself for the momentary flight of fancy. For Pete's sake, when had any man inconvenienced himself for her well-being? Never, that she could remember. But she didn't want Joshua that way, she reminded herself. The reminder, however, was becoming more and more difficult for her to believe.

Stepping forward, she lightly pressed the back of her hand against David's forehead. Fever all gone. The tension inside her eased a little more, and she looked at Joshua again. His jaw was shadowed with a morning beard, his hair dark and tousled, his eyelashes, black spiky fans. His shirt was wrinkled, probably damp from baby drool.

Maddie had never seen a more beautiful man in her life. When had he changed, she wondered? Or had she changed? Suddenly his eyes opened, his gaze finding hers with such speed and intensity that she stopped breathing. An old, old feeling, its origins in her childhood, tightened her stomach.

She felt *caught*.

Eight

Maddie breathed again, then followed old instincts. When caught, talk. A lot.

"You didn't wake me after an hour," she chided Joshua, flustered, eager to break the spell and alleviate the "caught" feeling. "It was nice of you to give me a break, but I hate the idea of you spending the night in that chair. Here, let me change him and feed him." She reached for David and walked toward the kitchen. "If you'll give me just a minute, I'll get you some coffee."

"Maddie?" Joshua's voice carried to her as she rounded the corner.

She stopped. "Yes?"

"You can skip the coffee. I'll leave in a minute or two."

His words spurred her into action again. "No, no, no." As David gummed her shoulder, Maddie pulled a bottle from the refrigerator and put it in the microwave to knock the chill off. After placing David in his high chair, she pulled out his antibiotic liquid. "Let me at least get you some coffee. If you can wait a little longer, I can fix you some breakfast and—"

"Hey." Joshua came up behind her. "Why the tizzy?"

Maddie paused as she poured the medicine into the infant spoon. Her heart was racing. Her mind was in turmoil. She felt all out of control. "Nobody's ever really been there for me when I needed help. Well, except for Emily and Jenna Jean, and sometimes Ben."

She gave David his medicine and watched him make a face. "Good boy," she murmured, shaking his formula and testing the temperature before she popped it in his mouth.

She finally looked up at Joshua. "I feel awkward. It means a lot to me, what you did last night—"

Joshua shrugged. "It wasn't a big deal."

"Yes, it was," she said emphatically. "It was a

big deal to me, and I don't know how to thank you.''

His gaze shifted with a hint of underlying sexuality. Maddie glanced down at her Betty Boop nightshirt and was certain she'd misread him.

''You're feeling grateful?''

''Yes.''

''How grateful?'' he asked in a deep, rumbly voice that did wicked things to her nerve endings. He moved closer.

Maddie swallowed, then gave a short laugh. Someone needed to set this man straight. ''I'm presently wearing a five-year-old nightshirt, feeding a baby, and I haven't checked the mirror, but I'm pretty sure my hair is sticking out in every possible direction on the compass. You couldn't possibly want me at this moment.'' Despite her protest she saw desire in his eyes. ''Not unless you're blind.''

He shook his head. ''Twenty-twenty vision.''

Perfect. Why didn't that surprise her? ''Or you're crazy.''

He gave a short laugh of his own and dipped his mouth to her neck. ''Now that is possible.''

Maddie closed her eyes against a flood of sensations. ''You can't want me. You can't. It's just not—''

His hand curved around her hip and stopped her

words. "I can," he told her, tugging her nightshirt up her thighs and sliding his fingers along her bare skin. He opened his mouth and gently sucked at the skin on her throat. "And I do."

Maddie felt like a toaster on broil. She bit back a moan when his fingers skimmed higher. Her nipples began to tingle and she had to fight the urge to rub her thighs together. "Joshua," she said.

"The question is do you want me?"

"Oh, help."

David whimpered, and Maddie opened her eyes. Muttering at herself, she stared at Joshua in accusation. "You're trying to wreck me."

"Think so?" His eyes were smoky gray, and his voice had a thigh-melting quality to it.

Maddie lifted her chin, seeing trouble in her future. "Yes, and you better stop it."

"Oh, yeah?"

"Yeah," she said, putting an extra note of belligerence in her voice.

"Turnabout's fair play. You wreck me, I wreck you. And now that I've sat up with David all night, I'd say you owe me."

Maddie's mouth went dry. She told herself it was shock and not excitement. He couldn't possibly mean— He didn't really expect her to show her gratitude in a sexual manner. A wicked voice inside her told her it would be the most enjoyable thank-you she'd delivered.

"Ice cream," Joshua said.

Completely befuddled, she stared at him. "Ice cream?"

"Friday night." He gave her a mock innocent look. "Can't go wrong with ice cream."

And Maddie realized she'd been deceived. Joshua was not a stick-in-the-mud. He was only disguised as one. He was, in fact, a wolf.

They didn't get the ice cream until later Friday night because Joshua had needed to take care of some horse business. By the time they arrived at the ice cream shop, it was mobbed, so they bought cartons and took them to Maddie's house.

Joshua was in a crazed mood. He hadn't felt like this in years. If he didn't have Maddie Palmer, he feared he was going to have to be committed. He felt like the Tasmanian Devil, and he was fighting the urge to take her on the kitchen table.

"Who did you say is taking care of David?" he asked, as she pulled chocolate, strawberry and butterscotch syrup out of the cupboard.

"My friend, Jenna Jean. She fussed at me for not calling her one of the nights he was sick, but I didn't even think of it. She's assistant DA," she told Joshua, "and she can tear a strip off you during an argument, so I just told her she could keep David another time.'' She pulled a can of whipped cream from the refrigerator and grinned. ''I picked tonight.''

Joshua looked from the whipped cream to Maddie and back to the whipped cream. In his wicked mind, wicked possibilities abounded. He cleared his throat. ''Do you like a little ice cream with your toppings?''

Her grin grew and she slit her eyes at him. ''A little ice cream. Are you a purist?''

He didn't feel the least bit pure around her. ''I take some chocolate syrup on top every now and then.''

She put Oreo cookies, sprinkles and bananas on the table. ''It sounds like you might need to expand your tastes.''

''I'm trying,'' Joshua muttered, watching her flit around the kitchen.

She played spoons for a few seconds, then put them on the table next to the bowls. She lifted her hand over the assortment of toppings. ''Well, what's your pleasure?''

''Tough to choose,'' he said.

''Then maybe I can help,'' she suggested, and opened the small cartons. ''You picked the lime sherbet. That limits the options. Even I don't put chocolate and lime together. But strawberry syrup? Bananas?''

She scooped the ice cream, poured the syrup and sliced half a banana. ''Whipped cream?'' she asked.

Joshua was having a tough time keeping his brain from sinking below his belt. ''Is it good?''

She frowned, then glanced at the can. ''It's not expired.'' She squirted a dot on her finger and licked it. ''Tastes good to me.'' She waited a moment and shrugged. ''You wanna try it?''

''Yeah,'' Joshua said.

She squirted more on her finger and lifted it presumably for him to swipe with his own finger. Instead, Joshua closed his hand around her wrist and lifted her finger to his mouth. He felt her jolt of surprise when he licked the cream…and her finger.

She jerked her hand away and looked down her nose at him. ''That was tricky.''

''If you would show a little pity,'' he said, emphasizing the word, ''I wouldn't have to resort to such measures.''

She stared at him for three seconds before he saw the beginning of a slow burn. ''Pity?''

''Yeah.'' He scooted the bowl toward him and took a spoonful. ''You kiss me, and just when I start to get out of control, you stop.'' He swallowed another bite and hoped it would cool the heat that seemed to burn inside him all the time lately. "You get close and then you move away. I wouldn't have thought you'd be such a tease, Maddie."

"Tease!" Looking hot enough to fry an egg on her body, she shook the can of whipped cream at him.

Joshua snickered. "Be careful where you point that. I was just kidding," he said, then added, "kinda."

"Kinda!" She pressed the nozzle on the whipped cream and sprayed him with it. Not just his hand or even his face, but his shirt. A dollop of it fell to his jeans.

Incredulous, Joshua looked at her. She appeared almost as appalled as he was.

"Oops." She gave a weak smile and put the can down. "Didn't mean to get your shirt."

Joshua shook his head. "You have a napkin?"

"Oh, sure. Just a second." She fluttered into action, pulling several from the counter and rushing to his side. She swiped at his shirt several times, then glanced down at his thigh.

Her brown-eyed gaze inched up his body and Joshua felt it, like he would have a series of open-mouth kisses on his bare skin. When she finally met his gaze, he could see bewilderment and arousal warring in her eyes.

She wore a sleeveless peach-colored dress that suited her personality. It was a warm evening, and her legs were bare except for a gold chain with hearts around her ankle and the sandals on her pretty feet. The swinging hem of her dress and the winking gold chain, along with her mischievous brown eyes and catch-me-if-you-can smile taunted the hell out of him.

Joshua gave in to one of the urges he'd been fighting all night. Sliding his hand just above her knee, he rubbed the naked silky skin of her shapely leg.

Maddie went still.

Her heart tripping over itself, she took a careful breath. There was something different about Joshua tonight. He seemed as if all he would need was a little push and he would be out of control.

The idea excited and unnerved her, and she wasn't totally certain how she wanted to respond. She did know, however, that she liked the way he looked at her, as if she were ice cream and he could eat her with a spoon. She liked the way his voice felt in her mind and sensitive places. She liked his hand on her leg way too much for uncertainty.

She cleared her throat. "The-uh-ice cream's melting."

He slid his fingers a little higher, and her chest tightened.

"Joshua," she managed, but the sound wasn't much of a protest.

"Maddie," he returned, his gaze knocking down her resistance. "When are you gonna put me out of my misery?"

Maddie sighed and slid her hand over his jaw. She liked the slightly raspy feel of his five o'clock shadow. Too much. "Joshua, you don't want to get involved with me."

He drew her between his legs so that she was flush against him. "I'm already involved."

"You are?"

He gave a slow nod and slid one of his legs between hers. "Yeah, and you are, too. Come closer, babe." He brushed his mouth over hers.

She felt herself sinking. Into his gaze, into his kiss, into him.

He pulled her down, making it so easy for her to slide her leg around and straddle him. "You should get involved with a different kind of woman," she warned him, and kissed him. "A woman who doesn't leave pacifiers in your driveway. Or get a flat tire you think you need to change."

She nuzzled his throat as he pushed her skirt up. "You should get involved with a woman who understands about studs and mares and settling and—''

''Maddie, I want you.'' He took her mouth, his tongue making love to hers.

It was a sensual, carnal kiss that made her heart tighten and her breath grow scarce. He slid his fingers between her legs to where she was moist and hot. Maddie gasped and ducked her head. ''I'm trying to warn you.''

He tipped her head upward and eased his finger inside her. ''You feel so good.''

She instinctively tightened. She wanted him. Oh, how she wanted him. ''We're not going to make it to the bedroom, are we?'' she whispered.

Joshua sucked at her bottom lip and gave a swift tug at her panties. There was a quick shredding sound. ''Not the first time,'' Joshua said.

Maddie unzipped his jeans and freed his hardened masculinity.

''That's right. Touch me,'' he urged, still snatching kisses, still caressing her intimately.

She moaned and stroked him. He was full with need, already moist with desire.

His rough sound of fascination and approval urged her on. She knew he was watching her. His arousal stirring hers, she rolled her forefinger over him, then lifted his honey to her mouth.

He closed his eyes as if in pain. ''Oh, Maddie.

Where have you been— Where—'' Breaking off, he dug into his pocket and pulled out a plastic packet.

She lost a little more of her heart when she saw that he'd come prepared. Considerate, solid, sexy.

He kissed her again, and the room felt as if it turned upside down. A moment passed, then another, and he was lifting her, positioning her over him. Then he gently guided her down until he filled her.

They stared at each other, joined intimately. Passion, desire, wonder. She undulated and watched him shudder. The shudder echoed inside her.

"Oh, lady." He wrapped his hands around her bottom and moved her in rhythm.

The pleasure grabbed and pulled at her. He looked at her as if she were the most beautiful woman in the world. She rode him, feeling his strength and need swell inside her.

He said her name, and a soft sound bubbled from her throat. He looked at her as if she were the only one who could satisfy him.

Maddie followed his faster rhythm, feeling the coil of sensation tighten inside her. Spinning higher and higher, she held tightly to him, never taking her gaze from his face.

Some part of her noticed he never took his gaze from her, either, and that he held her as tightly as she held him. He chanted her name again and again, but his eyes told her stories she was afraid to believe. His eyes told her this was more than want and need for him. His eyes told her that he loved her. That was when Maddie went over the edge. And Joshua tumbled after her.

The aftershocks rocked through them both, and they clung to each other, hearts pounding, breathing hard. He nudged her mouth up to his and kissed her gently, tenderly.

Then he looked at her and shook his head. "Oh, Maddie, heaven help me," he muttered in a husky voice. "I want you again."

She laughed weakly, laying her head on his shoulder. "Heaven help me. I want you again, too."

He squeezed her to him, and though he was still inside her, she knew what he was feeling. That close wasn't close enough. "Let's go upstairs."

She nodded. "Can you walk?"

His lips tilted into an affectionate grin. "Yeah."

"Show-off," she said, her legs still feeling like gelatin.

"It's okay," he said, shifting slightly, then standing. "I'll walk both of us."

"There's something very unfair about this." She tried to frown, but couldn't. She was too giddy.

He arched a dark eyebrow. "Unfair?"

"Yeah," she said, then impulsively picked up the can of whipped cream. "Let's see if I can improve the odds."

An hour and a half later, Joshua lay sprawled on her bed, trying to catch his breath. The can of whipped cream was empty. It had become an erotic battle of wills to see who would get the last dollop. Maddie had won. Just barely.

He stared down at her. She was a wholly feminine mess of tousled hair, bare skin, swollen lips from kissing and long lean limbs wrapped around him. She smelled like whipped cream and sex, and if he dwelled on that thought for longer than thirty seconds, then he would take her again.

At the moment her eyes were closed, and she breathed deeply, evenly. He might have thought she was sleeping except for the slight movement of her hand on his chest, back and forth, stroking gently. The tenderness in the gesture grabbed at his gut and twisted.

The way she affected him was amazing. When she made love with him, she held nothing back. Joshua had never experienced a woman giving to him so completely. Maddie wasn't one to sit back and be taken. She would do her share of the taking, too. The experience filled him with emotion. And questions.

Her eyes opened, and she met his gaze wordlessly.

"I have a personal question," he said.

"Okay. Ask."

"This man you were involved with for a long time…"

She nodded. "Clyde."

"He was away most of the time. I wondered if you made love with him like you did with me."

Her eyes widened, and she shifted slightly. "That is personal. Do you mean with whipped cream?"

He shrugged. "No. I mean with—" He searched for the right word. "With the same intensity."

She gave him a puzzled look. "Why do you ask?"

"If you did, then the guy probably didn't stay around much because he was afraid he'd die of cardiac arrest."

Maddie burst out laughing. "Oh, I don't think so." She shook her head at him, then her face grew more serious. "To answer your question, no, it's never been this intense for me." She paused, and her eyes darkened with a hint of uncertainty. "Too much?"

He shook his head. "No. Not at all."

He kissed her and felt her turn to liquid, and he

wanted her again. "We just had each other," he said in disbelief.

She sighed. "I know, and we've got to stop." Regret muted her voice. "I need to go get David. I don't want to terrify Jenna Jean this first time alone with him."

He fought disappointment and chuckled to himself. He was nuts. He gave her a quick kiss. "Let me drive you."

Surprise and pleasure softened her face. "Thank you. That would be very nice."

At first glance Jenna Jean Anderson was the antithesis of Maddie. Jenna had a cool, pulled-together image. Her brunette hair was neatly pulled back at the nape of her neck, and even in her jeans and blouse, she looked crisp and in control.

She probably wouldn't be caught dead in Maddie's dream catcher earrings, and she didn't seem the nurturing type. Maddie was warm and wild. Jenna was cool and rational.

Joshua didn't understand the close association between the two until Maddie mentioned how long they had been friends. "Jenna Jean and I have known each other since I was six and she was seven."

Jenna lifted a dark eyebrow. "I go by Jenna," she said to Joshua, then looked at Maddie. "Still pushing the age factor, I see."

Maddie grinned. "Age before beauty. How did Davey do?"

Jenna's face softened slightly. "David was divine. We discussed one of my cases and he agrees with my plans to ask for the maximum on a repeat DWI. I think he's gifted," Jenna continued. "I'm not kidding. He seemed as if he was listening to every single word. He was smiling and talking back to me."

Maddie slid a quick, sly glance to Joshua. "Did he offer any other suggestions?"

"No, but he's very discriminating. He yawned when I told him about my boss."

"Everybody yawns when you talk about your boss," Maddie said. "I take it he's asleep right now?"

"In my bedroom in the portable crib you brought."

"Okay," Maddie said, walking toward the hallway. "Back in a minute."

Jenna immediately turned to Joshua with an assessing glance. "So you're the man who helped deliver David?"

Joshua nodded. "I did."

"Maddie mentioned you run a horse farm. That can be a little risky, can't it?"

"It can be, depending how you run your business,'' he said, wondering where she was heading with her questions.

She casually gestured toward the sofa, but Joshua would swear she was weighing his every move. "And what about yours?" she asked.

"Are you asking if I'm solvent?"

She didn't miss a beat. "Not really, but that's an interesting question if you'd like to answer it."

He sat down and began to get a hint of her courtroom tactics. "I'm solvent."

Jenna nodded solemnly. "Maddie also mentioned you have a teenage son. Do you like children?"

He shrugged. "I like kids, some more than others."

She considered that, then folded her hands in front of her. "I suppose that's fair." She paused again, thinking. Her lips twitched. "Maddie has always had a—" she searched for the word "talent for—"

"Unfortunate experiences with authority figures," Joshua finished for her. "Or trouble."

"She's not a troublemaker," Jenna insisted, and Joshua liked her for defending Maddie. "She just gets caught. People closely associated with her develop a tolerance for—"

"Messes," Joshua finished again.

Jenna nodded. "Yes. Do you think of yourself as a flexible type of individual?"

He could have been offended if he didn't understand the basis for her questions. "Flexible to a point. I've got my limits. But, Jenna, are you sure we don't need a couple of witnesses and a Bible for this discussion?"

She struggled with a smile because she liked being in control, and he wasn't letting her. "I hope you're smarter than Clyde was. He didn't know what he had. Maddie's changed," Jenna continued. "She's not going to settle anymore."

Settle for what? he wanted to ask, but Maddie breezed back into the room. And Joshua was left with a question that lingered.

Nine

"Sighing, swooning," Jenna Jean said as she, Maddie, and Emily sat by Emily's mother's swimming pool. "You're disgusting."

"I know," Maddie agreed with a smile she knew was ridiculously huge. Nothing could dispel her great mood. "You ought to try a little sighing and swooning, yourself, Jenna Jean." Turning down the volume on the CD boom box, Maddie gave an exaggerated sigh and made a thumping motion with her hand over her heart. "Besides, I've got a good reason for it, and you've met him."

"Told you she was loopy. He's better than

Clyde, though, God rest his soul,'' Jenna Jean conceded.

Emily rubbed in sunscreen and frowned at the clouds. "When do I get to meet him?"

"I don't know. Joshua is out of town this weekend for some kind of Horse Breeder's Association meeting. Since you and Beau don't get to town very often…"

Emily sipped her lemonade. "We'll have to plan something then. With their mutual interest in horses, I think Joshua and Beau would get along."

Jenna Jean sat up and laughed. "Who would have thought our Emily would marry a cowboy?"

"Well," Emily said with a sly expression, "if I couldn't be a cowboy, marrying one was the next best thing." She glanced at Maddie. "I remember being afraid Maddie would turn into a rock groupie."

Maddie made a face. "I never liked the idea of being one of many. I wanted to be one, period. Maybe that's why Joshua has turned my head. He's different. He doesn't look at me and think 'temporary fling.' He's not that kind of man, and he wants me." He wants me. The notion still knocked her off-kilter.

The whole subject made her nervous and excited, unable to sit still. She stood and began to pace. "He's too good to be true. It's like one of those 'find what's wrong with this picture' exercises we did when we were kids. I keep looking for reasons why it won't work, and he keeps eliminating them. He calls me regularly,'' she said in amazement, because it was a novel experience for her.

Maddie shook her head and thought of David and how much she had changed over the last year. ''I just don't want to mess up this time.'' For all her supposed swooning and sighing, she wrestled with an ever present fear. ''I don't want to be foolish.''   ''You won't,'' Jenna Jean said to her. ''You've got your head on straight, and I think Joshua Blackwell knows he has found one in a million.''

''If he makes you happy, that's what matters,'' Emily said.

''But if he treats you bad,'' Jenna Jean began, and stood.

''We'll get him,'' Emily and Jenna Jean finished together.

Jenna Jean smiled. ''Now are you two going to be sun princesses all day or are you going to get wet? Last one in the pool is a rotten egg.''

''Looks like a sky full of diamonds,'' Maddie said as she lay on the blanket with Joshua. They'd gone out to dinner, and since it was such a warm, clear night, he'd brought her up to his hill. She could feel his warm gaze on her.

"Who has given you diamonds?"

Maddie's heart jumped, but she laughed to cover it. "More likely cubic zirconia or Austrian crystal."

"Did you miss the rocks?"

He took her hand, and she looked at him. "Diamonds?" she asked, and he nodded. Maddie thought about it. "No," she said, "and yes."

"Uh-huh," he said, looking at her as if she made no sense at all.

Maddie propped herself up on her elbow. "In itself I know the dollar figure on a gift is unimportant. I think it's more the symbolism behind it— that somebody would think I'm that important." She searched his gaze. "Does that make any sense?"

"I think so. What kind of presents did Clyde give you?"

Maddie chuckled again. "You mean when he remembered."

Joshua narrowed his eyes.

Maddie had to think. Clyde had been forgetful. "He gave me a lot of CDs that he liked, several demo tapes, some silver earrings from Mexico." She laughed in recollection. "He brought me peanut brittle once, but he ended up eating it. I never did like peanut brittle,'' she mused, then looked at Joshua and tried to read his expression. ''What are you thinking? Say it out loud.''

''Clyde sounds like he was a self-absorbed son-ovabitch.''

Maddie nodded and smiled. ''Yep, I guess he was.''

''Then why did you stay with him so long?''

Maddie sighed, sat up and drew her legs to her chest. ''I don't know. It was easier to stay with him than break it off. I think we were more of a habit for each other, and there was some security in that. People have all kinds of habits. Like you,'' she said, more than willing to turn the conversation away from herself.

''Me?''

''Sure. Why haven't you gotten involved with a woman for so many years?''

He shrugged. ''I've been busy.''

Maddie rolled her eyes. ''Lame, lame, lame.''

He wrapped his hand around her wrist and pulled her against his chest in a swift, economical motion. ''Who are you calling lame?'' he asked, his eyes playfully warning, yet sexually intense.

Maddie jutted out her chin. ''You.''

''I've been busy.''

''You've been wearing blinders,'' Maddie told him, forcing herself to concentrate as he slid his hands up the sides of her breasts. "You've cut yourself off from the female gender."

He shifted his pelvis so that she could feel his hardness against her. "Maybe I just didn't come across anyone who tripped my trigger."

She laughed breathlessly. "That's what you call it? Your trigger."

"Yeah," he said, skimming his hands down to her hips. "So what are you gonna do about it?"

It was one sexy, irresistible dare, and he made her want so much she felt like screaming. She shook her head and make a tsking sound. "I never would have thought you would be the type to go for this kind of outdoor activity."

His eyes darkened dangerously. "Is that so?" He rolled over so that she was beneath him. "And what type am I?"

Oops. Her stomach took a dip when he pressed his open mouth against her throat. "Type?" she repeated, hedging. She couldn't tell him what she'd really thought of him.

"*Yeah.* You think I'm the kind who draws the shades, turns out the light and makes love in the bed in the dark."

"Thought," she corrected. "What are you doing to my shorts?"

"Helping," he murmured, "to educate you about what kind of man I am."

The cool night air whispered over her skin, then his warm hands caressed her. Her heart raced, and she trembled. "I thought you'd already done that."

"Oh, baby, I've just gotten started with you."

A warning or a promise? An illicit thrill ran through her as he kissed her. He wasn't actually going to take her on this hill among the stars, was he? Maddie remembered the whipped cream and groaned.

He slipped one of his hands up her shirt and rubbed her already stiff nipple. "I think it's about time I tripped your trigger," Joshua said as he began to make a slow, breathtaking journey down her body with his mouth.

No one had ever made her feel this wanted. The feeling turned her to liquid. How did he do this to her? Fighting for a shred of sanity, Maddie joked, "Last time I looked, I didn't have a trigger."

He swirled his tongue around her belly button, and she shuddered. "Then I'll make you see stars," he promised, lowering his mouth again, this time between her thighs to the aching, moist heart of her. "I'll make you see stars inside."

Joshua's hands held her hips, and his tongue made magic. But it was his intimate words, his sounds of approval, need and want that sent her over and over again. And even when Maddie closed her eyes, she saw stars.

* * *

When he took her home that night, Maddie felt
very vulnerable to him. It scared her, because she
felt as if she would do anything for him. That could
be dangerous. Then she looked at him, though, and
saw his solid strength stamped across his features,
across his body. He was a kind man, she reminded
herself. A good man, who wouldn't take advantage
of her. She could trust him.

Joshua came inside with her and talked with Ben
for a few moments while she checked on David.
Ben had taken care of David for the evening, in-
sisting her son needed regular exposure to male
influence, so he wouldn't end up thinking like a
woman.

At another time she would have argued with
him, but tonight she was in a daze. When she
walked downstairs, Ben was gone.

"He needed to get to his job," Joshua said.

Maddie nodded. "Bouncing at the bar. Well, my
brother did a pretty good job. David's diaper isn't
on backward or anything."

Joshua chuckled, then pulled her to him.
"You're an incredible woman, Maddie. I've never
met anyone like you."

"Is that good or bad?"

"Good," he said. "Very good."

Swallowing a lump in her throat, Maddie took
her heart in her hand. "I feel the same way about

you. I've never met a man like you, who makes me—" She looked into his eyes. "Makes me feel like this." And hope. And believe.

"You're so honest and generous." He shook his head as if he couldn't believe she existed. "Most women want something back," he said. "Marriage or money. They want ownership. But you—" He cupped his hand under her jaw. "You understand. You don't have to have a man on a leash to know you've got him how it counts."

An unsettling sensation fluttered in her stomach. "On a leash?"

"Yeah. You're an incredibly rare woman," he told her, "because you don't have to have marriage."

Oh, yes I do. I thought you knew that. She felt as if she were on an elevator and the cable had just been cut. She couldn't have said a word if she'd had one in her head. Joshua continued to talk, but she didn't hear him.

She had been fooled again. Her stomach twisted violently. She had fooled herself again. Why had she been so stupid? Why had she thought he would see her differently than any other man? Just because he was solid and dependable? Just because he had helped deliver her baby, change a flat tire and relieved her that night David had been sick?

God, she hurt. She'd never hurt like this for a

man. With Clyde she'd never really trusted him enough to put her hope in the future. But she'd allowed herself to hope with Joshua. She had been so totally and incredibly foolish. He was just like other men, except in a different wrapping.

He was still touching her, but she was so physically frozen she couldn't feel it. She watched his mouth form words. He lowered his head to hers as if he was going to kiss her and she flinched.

He looked at her quizzically. "You okay?"

She blinked away the fog and nodded. A lie.

He kissed her lightly. "See you Wednesday."

No. She meant to shake her head, but she moved it in a circle. *The meals.* Her mind raced. What would she do about the meals?

"G'night, babe," he said, then walked out the door.

As the door clicked shut, she whispered, "Goodbye, Joshua."

She felt so stupid and angry she needed to break something. "I'm not going to cry," she told herself in a shaky voice. "I'm not going to cry."

Staring down at her feet, she willed them to move and headed for the kitchen, still chanting, "I'm not going to cry."

She opened the cupboard and pulled out a jelly glass and threw it hard into the sink. "He's not worth it."

Such crazy dreams she'd had. So crazy she wouldn't even share them with anyone. She pulled out another jelly glass and looked at it.

"My heart isn't broken."

Liar.

Her stomach twisted. Her throat was so tight her voice was hoarse. "It's only bruised," she insisted, and smashed the glass into the sink.

She looked for another jelly glass, but paused, her mind flying in a million directions. "Why did I do this to myself?"

She felt as if her chest was in a vise. Her eyes burned. "I'm not going to cry," she said around the huge lump in her throat. But her cheeks were wet from tears. Another lie. Maddie's shoulders sank. A deep, aching disappointment shuddered through her. Disappointment in herself and Joshua. No more lies, she thought, wiping her cheeks and letting the tears flow. She'd told herself too many.

Joshua looked at the chicken parmesan and frowned. The chicken was good, but he hadn't talked to Maddie in three days. He was beginning to wonder if she was avoiding him.

"When did you say she came?" he asked Patrick again.

Patrick swallowed a bite. "I'd just gotten home from school. She wasn't here but a minute." He took a gulp of milk. "Said she was in a big hurry." He stuffed half a roll in his mouth.

Joshua felt doubt tugging at him. Doubt and disappointment. "Did she say anything else?"

Patrick's eyebrows furrowed in concentration, and he shook his head. Then he stopped abruptly, his face clearing. "Oh, yeah."

Joshua felt a trickle of relief and he rolled his shoulders. A message for him, he thought. An explanation about where she'd been. A promise to call.

Patrick grinned and talked around a bite of chicken. "She said to put the Jell-O in the fridge."

Joshua tried calling her twice a day for the next several days. If his schedule hadn't been so packed and he hadn't been working from dawn to dusk, he would have driven into town to see her. As it was, he barely had time to eat.

Since he'd first made love to Maddie, he'd dreamed every night, all night. One of those crazy, inexplicable things, he'd told himself. Probably related to hormones. Lately when he slept, he only had snatches of dreams. They didn't last the whole night. He couldn't explain the change. He sure as hell didn't have the time or energy to try.

Lack of energy or time, however, didn't stop him from wondering what was going on with Maddie. By Wednesday he decided to devote the afternoon and evening to paperwork so he wouldn't miss her.

He heard the buzz of her muffler long before she pulled in front of his house. At the sound of her cutting her engine, Joshua opened the door to offer his help, but she was already moving quickly toward his front porch. Her hair bounced with her movements. Her skirt swished against her legs. Her vitality was contagious. He noticed a Band-Aid on her ankle and wondered what she'd bumped into. At first glance she made his heart pound faster.

At second glance when her gaze briefly met his and her step faltered as if she wasn't pleased to see him, he immediately knew something was wrong.

"Hi. Sunny today, isn't it?" she said as she flitted past him. "I brought a meat 'n' potatoes meal tonight. Pepper steak, mashed potatoes and gravy, and green beans. Hope you and Patrick enjoy it. Speaking of Patrick, where is he?"

Following her into the kitchen, Joshua frowned. "He stayed after school for a special computer class. Where have—"

"Computer," Maddie repeated brightly. A little too brightly, he thought. "That's great. I bet he's good with computers."

Joshua nodded. "Yes, but—"

"I put the pudding in the fridge. Sorry I've gotta

run, but I need to pick up Davey at the sitter,'' she said as she practically raced for the door. ''It was nice seeing—''

Just as she reached for the door, he stepped in front of her and blocked her. He felt like a stud trying to corral a jittery female. ''What's going on?''

She met his gaze again briefly, then glanced away and shrugged. ''It's a busy day. I need to pick up Davey from the sitter.''

''Have you gotten my telephone messages?''

She crossed her arms over her chest and took a deep breath. She seemed to be studying the toe of her shoe. ''Yes.''

He wondered ironically where the chatterbox had gone. ''Did you think about returning my calls?''

She made a restless move with her arms. ''Yes.''

Lord, he felt like he was pulling teeth. ''Any particular reason you didn't?''

She nodded. ''Yes.''

Joshua waited in silence, but she said nothing. He ground his teeth together. ''Would you like to share it with me?''

She paused as if she wasn't at all certain she wanted to share anything with him, and her hesitation got under his skin. He swore under his breath. ''Okay, Maddie, quit playing chicken,'' he said, and watched her head snap upward. He pulled her against him and struggled with an urge to kiss the resistance out of her. "Tell me what the hell is going on. The last time I was with you we were as close as two people can get. The last time we were together we made love."

Her brown gaze finally met his, defiant, yet disappointed in a way that made his gut sink. "I screwed up," she said flatly. "I thought you and I wanted the same thing, but I was wrong. I can't be with you that way anymore."

Ten

Joshua thought he would have recovered more quickly if she'd kicked him in the groin. This sharp pain, however, was much higher. He stared at her. "What in hell are you talking about?"

"Exactly what I said," she told him, and wiggled as if she was trying to get away from him.

Joshua instinctively tightened his hands. "What is this stuff about not wanting the same thing?"

She took a deep breath. "We don't. I want a more permanent relationship. I thought you did, too, but you don't. My fault," she said quickly in a soft voice. "I'm not blaming you. I'm not trying to trick you or change you, but I want more than I've had in the past.'' She shook her head. ''I can't settle for what I had before. I have someone else to think about now. Davey.''

Settle. Now he knew what Jenna Jean had meant. He bit back a silent oath.

She gave a shaky, terrible attempt at a smile and made a choking sound he'd bet she intended as a laugh. ''And call me crazy, but maybe there's somebody out there who will look at me and see more than a good time.''

Everything inside him roared in protest. ''You're more than a good—''

She held up a hand and shook her head. ''Joshua, this isn't necessary. I know you're trying to be kind, but I don't need your reassurance. I don't blame you. I understand what you want. I simply can't give it, and this whole thing is embarrassing for me, so I'd just like to go.'' She looked away from him and waited a few seconds. ''Please.''

He couldn't let her go. His hands, his body, his mind would not let her go. It was more than unacceptable. It was untenable. He shook his head, rejecting everything she'd said. ''No. I—''

The door whooshed open into Maddie, pushing both of them backward. He heard Patrick call out, ''I'm home!''

Maddie used the moment to pry Joshua's fingers from her arms and step away from him. He watched her force a smile for his son and greet him. "I've gotta run. I'll see you two next week. Take care, now."

She whirled through the open doorway and ran down the steps. She started her engine, her muffler scaring the birds out of the trees. Fighting the urge to stop her, Joshua clenched his fists and knew with sinking certainty that he had just let the best thing that had happened to him slip right through his fingers.

"Dad. Hey, Dad," Patrick said for the third time. "What's with you and Maddie? I thought you and she were—"

Tearing his gaze from the exhaust Maddie's car had left in its wake, Joshua looked at Patrick and saw the questions all over his son's face. He sighed. "I thought we were, too," he muttered, and closed the door behind them.

"So what happened? Did you dump her or something?" Patrick asked as he followed Joshua into the kitchen.

The irony was enough to make him choke. Joshua shook his head. "No. She dumped me."

Patrick's eyes rounded. "No way!"

His chest hurt, and he felt a gnawing ache he

was determined to categorize as hunger for dinner. "Yes. She dumped me."

"Geez, Dad. What did you do? Maddie's so cool. She would have to be really ticked off to dump you, wouldn't she?"

The truth was painfully clear to Joshua. Maddie had opened her heart to him and let him in. She had been warm and willing and loving in a way no one had ever been to him.

Maddie had not been the one to mess up.

"I screwed up," he said to Patrick. It was simple. He'd rolled the dice and lost, and Joshua fought the certain, but sickening feeling that this loss could have a significant impact on the rest of his life.

Joshua's dreams faded completely away. There wasn't even a glimmer of any nocturnal vision that graced him. His nights returned to drab, endless black deserts. It was like a winter that wouldn't end. He dreaded going to bed at night and hated the way he felt when he woke in the morning.

He told himself there were advantages to getting back his precious peace and quiet. He wasn't changing tires in the rain. He wasn't delivering pacifiers to single mothers. He wasn't losing sleep while he rocked a fretful baby with an ear infection. It had been weeks since the birds in his trees had exhibited signs of nervous breakdowns from the sound of Maddie's muffler, because she'd delivered the last few meals via her brother. Major didn't bark his head off when she came within earshot.

Everything was quieter. It was an improvement, he insisted. He liked it better this way. He liked his life calm and without disruptions.

But he felt like a dried-up leaf. Maddie had brought the rain, but she'd also brought the sunshine. She had kicked the life back into him. She had made him aware of all he'd been missing the past years. She'd given him a taste of possibilities. She'd made him want, then satisfied him. She'd made him feel, and he almost resented her for that. Not feeling had been easier.

It was Wednesday night, and Joshua heard Benjamin Palmer buzz to a stop on his Harley. Patrick shot up from the kitchen table and walked to open the front door. "Wonder what she sent this time," he said.

"I don't know," Joshua muttered, and joined his son.

With eyes so like Maddie's, Ben shot Joshua a cocky, denigrating glance, then nodded at Patrick. "How ya doing, bud?"

"Pretty good. School will be out in a few weeks. I can't wait."

Brooding, Joshua watched the two as they conversed. He was fairly certain the only reason Ben hadn't added arsenic to the food was because of Patrick.

"She sent chicken stir-fry and rice. You'll probably need to heat it up. The brownies are awesome. I negotiated a batch in trade," Ben said, grinning slyly at Patrick.

"You're lucky," Patrick said. "You can eat Maddie's food anytime."

"Thank you for bringing the meal," Joshua told Ben. "I'd appreciate it if you'd tell Maddie I said thank you, too."

Ben looked at him as if he'd just as soon spit at him. "It's not gonna make a helluva big difference. You screwed up."

Joshua didn't blink. "Yeah, I did."

Ben's eyes widened briefly in surprise, then he turned back to chat with Patrick.

When he started to leave, Joshua gave in to a growing need to know what Maddie was doing. "How is she?"

Ben paused. "Fine," he said. "She's busy, but she always worked at staying busy when something was bothering her. Right now an IRS auditor is trying to make sense of last year's return."

Joshua frowned. He was reasonably certain tax

accounting wasn't Maddie's forte. "Has she got a tax accountant?"

"I don't think so. What do you care?" he asked belligerently. "All you wanted was a roll in the—"

He didn't get out the rest of his statement before something inside Joshua snapped and he shoved Ben against the wall. "I told you," he said, meeting the younger man's defiant gaze, "I screwed up. I'm paying for it. She's gone, and I wake up knowing it every single day."

Ben shrugged against the hold and stared at him. "Well, if you're that unhappy about it, and you're damn sure you're not going to hurt her again, then why don't you do something about it?"

"Everywhere But The Moon Tours," Maddie said into the phone, wishing she could go to the moon. "This is Maddie. How can I help you?"

After spending her lunch hour trying to reason with the IRS representative, she was convinced the man had ice water in his veins instead of blood. She was also convinced that one of the all-time great American lies was, "Hello, I'm with the IRS, and I'm here to help you."

Pushing aside her anxiety about her audit, she listened to the customer's request for airline tickets and punched out the information on her keyboard, then gave a quote.

"Which credit card—" She faltered when a cup of ice cream and a pink plastic spoon was placed on her desk in front of her. She slowly glanced up and saw a pair of hard muscular thighs encased in snug denim, a leather belt and gold buckle, a flat abdomen, well-developed chest and broad shoulders. She looked up a little farther and saw Joshua regarding her intently. Her heart slammed into overdrive.

The customer chanted the numbers to his credit card, but Maddie didn't take them down. She shook her head and looked away from Joshua. "I'm sorry. Could you repeat that, please?"

She had to shade her eyes to focus, but she managed to get the appropriate information and ring off. She looked at Joshua again and blinked to make sure she hadn't imagined him. Again.

"Hi," she said. She'd delayed seeing him because she'd known it would knock her sideways. She'd hoped time would soften the impact. It hadn't.

"Hi," he said, and his voice did the same scary, wonderful thing to her stomach.

She took a careful breath and tried not to stare. He looked so good, but was so bad for her. "Well, what are you doing here?"

He nodded toward the ice cream. "You never got to eat your ice cream that night we were together."

She glanced at it and fought a sensual, emotional tidal wave. The night they'd made love. She pushed her hair back from her face and produced a smile. "What a nice surprise," she murmured, and pulled off the top.

Whipped cream. A lump formed in her throat.

"Underneath the butterscotch syrup and sprinkles there is some ice cream," he said in a wry tone.

How was she going to eat this? All she could think of was the erotic taste of Joshua and whipped cream. Her mind was filled with the image of Joshua taking her, and her taking him.

Extremely conscious of his gaze on her, she forced a small bite in her mouth. "It's delicious."

"Good." He sat on the edge of her desk. "I wondered if you would go with me for ice cream on Friday."

She had wondered if he would come around again. She had hoped for it, feared it, avoided it. She'd even bribed Ben to deliver Joshua's meals so she wouldn't have to face him. Cowardly? Perhaps. Maddie preferred to view it as prudent. While she'd never been particularly prudent before, she thought it might be a good idea to develop the attribute.

So far it went against her grain. But she wasn't giving up yet. She had too much to lose.

Not only that, she was wearing three guardian angel pins under her collar to protect her from temptation. Temptation was sitting right in front her, and it wasn't the ice cream.

She cleared her throat. "I don't think that's a good idea."

He leaned closer. "Why not?"

He made the words sound intimate; his mouth was close, and she could see the wanting in his gaze. The same wanting she felt inside. It would be so easy to lift her lips for him to take.

His eyes could turn her to liquid, his voice dissolved her resolve. He was the best and worst kind of temptation. *Lead me not into temptation,* Maddie thought desperately. *I have no problem getting there all by myself.*

She sucked in a deep breath and backed away. "Because you have a bad habit of melting my—" *Everything,* she thought. *You melt my everything.* But she glanced down at her disintegrating dessert and said, "Ice cream."

On Saturday morning she had the stereo cranked up to concert level. If she had to revisit her tax return for the tenth time, then U2 could help her through it. She'd set Davey's swing to rock for twenty minutes, and every now and then she tickled his toes and made kiss noises on his feet. She was flipping through old receipts and canceled checks when someone banged on her front door.

She debated answering it. So far, one charity and two religious organizations had solicited her. Grudgingly, she rose and opened the door.

Joshua and a preppy-looking man stood on her porch.

Maddie's gaze latched on to Joshua, and she felt that familiar, cursed, sinking sensation. What was he doing here? After turning down his offer for ice cream and anything else he might have in mind, she'd assumed he wouldn't come for her anymore. After all, Joshua could have any number of women. That fact did nothing to elevate her mood.

Irritated that she was going to have to shoo him away again, Maddie thought about her guardian angels and frowned. She was doing her best to fight her desire for Joshua and she could use some help.

Joshua's mouth was moving, but she couldn't quite make out his words. "Pardon?" she said.

With a wry half grin, he shook his head and walked past her to turn down the volume of the stereo. "I understand you've been going a couple of rounds with the IRS, so I brought a friend who can help. This is Roger Hensley. He's my tax accountant.''

Nonplussed, she hesitated, looking from Joshua to Roger. She extended her hand. "Thank you. It's very nice to meet you." She had no idea how to act toward Joshua. This went far beyond ice cream. It was thoughtful, considerate. She might almost believe she truly mattered to him. Her heart swelled in hope, and she scolded herself. She'd been fooled before.

"Maddie," Roger said, "do you mind letting me take a look at your return?''

Torn for only a second, she shook her head. "Not at all. I'd be very grate—" She broke off when Joshua caught her eye. The tension thrummed between them. There'd been gratitude and too much more, but she couldn't afford to turn down an offer of help at this stage. "I'd appreciate it," she said, then went to collect the forms.

Two hours later Roger had worked his accounting magic and straightened out her return. He gave her his business card as he left. "If the gladiator from the IRS has any questions, you can tell him to call me.''

She offered to pay him, but he held up his hands and assured her it was covered. After he was gone, she turned slowly to Joshua, who was holding

Davey as he slept. The image tugged at her heart, reminding her of secret wishes and dreams, reminding her of her foolish hopefulness. She tried to block her feelings.

It was nearly impossible. "That was very nice," she told him. "Why did you do it?"

Joshua looked momentarily uncomfortable. "You needed help. It wasn't difficult to arrange."

Maddie nodded and took Davey from Joshua. "No big deal?" she asked in a quiet voice. "No big deal to get a tax accountant to make a house call on a Saturday morning."

He shrugged. "He's an old friend. A nice guy."

"What did you give him?" When he looked as if he was going to deny it, she cut him off at the pass. "And don't lie."

"Discount stud service for his mare." His eyes glinted with sexual innuendo. "Don't worry, Maddie. No one will suffer."

She groaned and walked away, taking Davey to his crib. Her mind was whirling. Why was he doing this? It made no sense. Joshua had made it clear he wanted her for a good time. She'd made it clear she needed more now. So why was he playing with her? Why was he doing things for her?

Returning to the den, she confronted him. "I appreciate your friend's help with my taxes very much, Joshua. But I don't understand why you came to see me at work the other day or today."

He walked toward her. "I've missed you."

Her stomach turned a somersault. "You have?" She heard the cracked surprise in her own voice and cleared her throat.

"Yeah." He lifted a strand of hair from her cheek. "Have you missed me?" he asked in a low voice.

Too much. She swallowed. "I—uh—I thought it would be best if we didn't see each other."

Joshua nodded and moved closer. "I disagree."

Maddie stepped backward, trying to create some desperately needed space between them. "We want different things. You want fun. I need— Ouch!" Her heel banged against the baseboard.

"You rushed me," he told her in a mild tone.

She looked at him in confusion. "I rushed you?"

"I'd just gotten started and you decided it was over."

Despite his closeness, she tried to keep a clear head. "I thought it was best—"

"Best for who?" he demanded, trailing his fingertips down her bare arm.

She ignored the tingling sensation. "Best for both of us."

"Not for me," he told her, and lowered his mouth to hers.

She ducked her head and dodged him, barely. Oh, Lord, she could practically taste him, she thought, closing her eyes for a second.

He took a different tack and brushed his lips over her bangs. "I've missed you. I want to know that you've missed me, too."

Her heart squeezed tight. She feared saying yes to him, feared it would precipitate a slew of other *yes*es she shouldn't even be thinking. "That doesn't really matter," she insisted. "We want different things."

"Go to lunch with me," he said, dropping his mouth to her neck.

Maddie shook her head. "No."

"Tell me you've missed me."

"No." She whispered the lie and bit back a groan when he pressed against her from chest to thigh. He was strong, and he felt so right. But it was so wrong. She pushed against him and squeezed underneath his arm, holding out her hand for him to stop when he walked toward her again.

"We're nowhere near finished yet," he told her, determination stamped on his face.

The power of his confidence could have daunted her if she didn't have a stubborn will of her own. She suspected, however, that she was going to need more than three metal angels from the card shop, if she was going to stand her ground.

She lifted her chin. "You're not calling all the shots, Joshua. It takes two, and I don't want to play with you anymore."

His gaze skimmed over her possessively. "Then I'll have to change that, won't I? And, sweetheart, here's fair warning, I've just gotten started."

He walked out the door, leaving Maddie to wonder when salt-of-the-earth, stick-in-the-mud Joshua had turned into the very devil.

Eleven

By the time Joshua got out of the barn, Maddie was roaring up his lane, away from the house, away from him. Her muffler buzzed like a giant mutant bee.

Even in the rain he could see the exhaust from her tailpipe. He threw his rake to the ground and swore. His best opportunity for catching her in days, and he'd missed her.

The volume of her motor abruptly increased, and he narrowed his eyes. He jogged farther up the lane and saw an object lying in the road. Despite his ill mood, he chuckled when he identified it. This evening might turn around for him yet.

Turning out of Joshua's driveway, Maddie floored her accelerator and frowned at how loud her engine sounded. She couldn't hear her radio. She couldn't hear herself think. She checked on Davey. He looked numb.

Maddie supposed some might say she'd acted like a chicken by running in and out of Joshua's house so quickly. But she would disagree. She was trying to be prudent again.

Chicken.

"Prudent," she retorted aloud, but was barely able to hear herself.

She continued down the road when a siren sounded. Glancing in her rearview mirror, she cringed and immediately glanced at her speedometer. She wasn't speeding. What could be wrong?

She pulled to a stop on the side of the road and waited, a sense of dread settling in her stomach. She'd never dealt well with authority figures.

The officer strolled alongside her car. He tipped his hat. "Ma'am, are you aware that it's illegal to operate a vehicle without a muffler?"

Nonplussed, she shook her head. "But I have a muffler. I know I do. I know—"

The officer smiled and shook his head. "No ma'am, you don't, and I'm gonna have to give you a ticket."

"But—"

A truck came to a stop beside her. Joshua's truck, Maddie realized. She didn't know whether to duck or be relieved.

Getting out, he pulled something long and rusty from the bed of his truck. "Looking for this?" he asked Maddie with a smart-aleck grin.

"How are you, Abel?" he said to the officer. "Slow day when you pick on young mothers with babies, isn't it?"

Abel winced. "She's a mom? Damn, I didn't see a baby in there." He shoved his pad of tickets back into his pocket. "That her muffler?"

"Yep, she left it in my driveway."

"Okay, Josh. Make sure it gets fixed. Don't let me catch her without it again. Evening, ma'am," he said to Maddie, then strolled back to his car.

"Male chauvinist," she muttered under her breath, and met Joshua's gaze. "May I have my muffler, please?"

"Sure," he said, putting the rusted metal in her back seat. "But if another cop stops you, you'll probably get a ticket."

She brushed her hair back in frustration. "How am I supposed to get to a service station to get it fixed?"

He leaned against her window. "I know a guy who might be willing to fix it for you tonight."

Maddie was skeptical. "And charge me an arm and a leg?"

Joshua shook his head. "No more than you'll pay tomorrow in town."

"Lead on," Maddie said.

Joshua's lips tilted in a wicked grin. "You can join us for dinner."

Maddie's stomach flipped. Why did he make her feel like she was going to be dinner?

An hour later, after they'd finished the meal and Patrick had disappeared into his bedroom to do homework, Maddie put Davey down for a nap on a blanket. She'd been leery of leaving him there with Major so close by, but the dog acted as if it was his job to watch the baby. He sat and watched, and after a few minutes, closed his eyes.

Joshua urged her outside on the front porch. "C'mon, you can see him through the door. It's stopped raining."

Weary of fighting him, Maddie threw in the towel for the evening. She wouldn't be staying much longer because her muffler would be fixed, and he hadn't jumped her during dinner.

She looked up at the winking stars in the sky and took a deep breath. "It really is beautiful, here. You don't have to contend with the lights from the city."

He came to stand behind her. "Yeah. It reminds

me of that night we were together on the hill," he murmured.

Maddie's insides tightened in remembrance. Joshua had been tenderly persistent for her pleasure. He had held her as if he would never let go, made love to her as if she were the most important woman in the world to him. He'd made her giddy.

She felt his hand on her hair and held her breath.

"I've never wanted a woman like I want you, Maddie."

She swallowed past her tight throat. "It's been a long time for you," she said. "That's all."

He gave a dry chuckle. "It would be a helluva lot easier if that was all." He slid his hand around her waist and pulled her against him. "What would you think if I told you I hadn't dreamed in years?"

She knew she should move away, but his statement distracted her, surprised her. She looked up at him. "What?"

"What would you think if I told you I hadn't dreamed in years?"

Maddie shook her head. The idea was difficult to comprehend. "I can't imagine it. How can you not dream? You go to bed at night and you dream."

"Not me," he said, and sifted his fingers through her hair. "I didn't dream for years."

"But that changed?"

"Yeah." He continued to stroke her hair. His touch was both soothing and sensual, and she would stop him. In a minute.

"When did you dream again?"

"The first time?"

She nodded, and his fingers slid down her neck. Her insides dipped and swayed. It was easy and hard to be held by him. Easy because it felt so good and right. Hard because she knew better.

"The first time I had a dream was when you kissed me for changing your tire."

Maddie's heart stopped. "What?"

His gaze met hers and he continued to stroke downward. "I dreamed the night you kissed me."

"What did you dream?"

He wore an expression of mingled disgust and disbelief. "Buttercups."

She couldn't suppress a light laugh. "How did it feel to dream again?"

"I liked it, but I didn't dream again until you kissed me again."

A smidgen of doubt crept in. "That's odd," she said.

"No kidding," Joshua muttered. "I thought it was coincidence until it happened again. Strange as hell."

She was torn. He sounded as skeptical as she felt.

His gaze locked on hers, he slid his fingers underneath the top of her blouse to her breasts. "Oh, Maddie, you have no idea what you do to me." He lowered his mouth to hers and plucked at her nipple.

She should be saying no right now, she thought, but her mouth was opening to him, her tongue wrapping around his in an intimate caress. She should be pushing his hand away, but her breast was swollen and budding beneath his touch.

She felt like a meteor shower was falling inside her, and she didn't want it to stop. If she had superpowers, she could pull back right now, but Maddie had always been extremely human. Never more human than right now.

"Oh, Maddie, I want you," he murmured against her mouth. "I want you back."

In the back of her mind she heard a voice, *Fool me once, shame on you. Fool me twice, shame on me.* Her heart tightened, and her doubts tumbled through her.

"You've turned me upside down," Joshua said, kissing her neck, still fondling her breasts. "Making me dream, then making me stop when you cut me off."

"Cut you off?" she repeated, grasping for a shred of sanity. She was torn between fear and arousal.

"Oh, yeah. The first time we made love, I dreamed the whole night through. When you dumped me, the dreams completely stopped."

Maddie backed away and stared at Joshua. Her head was reeling. She felt as if she were on a see-saw, and she didn't know which way to go. To believe or not believe. He looked trustworthy. He sounded as if he was telling the truth. But she'd been fooled before.

"Are you telling me you haven't dreamed since we made love?" she asked, watching him closely.

He shook his head slowly. "A few quick, vague visions, but no real dreams. I haven't dreamed at all since we were together under the stars."

Maddie simply couldn't believe she could have that kind of impact on a man, especially a man like Joshua.

"You don't look like you believe me," he said.

"I'm having a very difficult time," she confessed. "Do you know what it sounds like?"

He leaned against the railing and crossed his arms over his chest. "What?"

"The most original line for getting laid I've ever heard."

"Well, if it isn't Mr. Sleaze," Jenna Jean Anderson said, looking down her slim nose at him.

Joshua swallowed a sigh. Not an auspicious beginning, he thought. He was getting nowhere fast with Maddie, and the thought of not having her in his future turned his stomach. "I need your help," he said bluntly.

Her eyes widened slightly. "Help? Why should I help you? You hurt my friend. You," she said, pointing her finger at him, "Mr. Studfarm Owner—"

"I screwed up," he said, finishing for her. "She's the best thing that ever happened to me, and I want her back." He met her doubtful gaze without flinching. "I think underneath it all she might want me, too. Are you letting me in, or not?"

She hesitated a long moment, then opened the door wider. "If you make me regret this, I'll find a way to torture you the rest of your life."

"I don't doubt it," he muttered, but walked inside her house.

"Have a seat." She motioned toward the sofa. "I haven't talked to Maddie in a few days. What have you done so far?"

In no mood for sitting, he paced. "I took her ice cream at work, got a tax accountant to straighten out her IRS problems and got her out of a ticket when her muffler fell off her car."

Jenna made a noise of disgust. "Maui strikes

again.'' Her face cleared. ''I'm impressed with the tax accountant. Nice touch.''

''Thanks. It didn't work.''

''When you apologized,'' Jenna began, and she must have read his expression. She rolled her eyes. ''Oh, no, you didn't apologize.''

He threw out his hands. ''What do I apologize for? All I did was tell her she was an incredible woman and how special she was because she didn't need marriage.'' He shook his head. ''How was I supposed to know she was even thinking about anything permanent?''

Jenna sighed. ''I need some wine. Do you want some wine?''

''No. I've already tried whiskey. It doesn't work.''

Jenna disappeared into the kitchen and returned with a glass. She sank into an overstuffed chair. ''Would you please sit down?''

Joshua reluctantly sat.

''Okay, let's take this from the top. First the apology. Even if you don't think you said anything wrong, you can apologize for hurting her feelings.'' She took a sip. ''There's also the matter of how you feel about a permanent, committed relationship.''

''I want Maddie in my life.''

"For how long?" Jenna asked, regarding him carefully.

Joshua had dodged this question with himself. The idea of making a commitment, even in his mind, when Maddie would barely accept his phone calls made him itch. In most instances he preferred hedging his bets.

"That's something Maddie and I will have to figure out," he said.

She lifted her eyebrows and seemed to consider him yet again. "I'm going to tell you something about Maddie. She has never had a man court her. She might deny that she would want such a thing, but she wouldn't be telling the truth. She was hooked up with Clyde for a long time, but he never bothered to find out what she wanted."

Joshua's mind immediately whipped through the little hints Maddie had innocently given him in their various conversations. Remembering one in particular, he swore under his breath and shook his head.

"What's wrong?"

"I can't play a kazoo, let alone a guitar," Joshua growled.

Maddie sang along with Bryan White and fed Davey his first rice cereal. She couldn't tell if he liked it or not, since most of it was on his hands and face. Unfortunately he'd flung some of it on her. Good thing it was Sunday morning and no one would see her in her current state. She'd pulled her hair into a high ponytail and wore an ancient T-shirt and denim cutoffs.

Watching his eyes dance and his feet kick, she smiled. His vibrant personality was becoming more apparent with each passing day. Bright and curious, he was a happy baby, but he had a little stubborn streak. He didn't sleep too much. Maddie suspected he didn't want to miss anything.

Maddie loved it when he gurgled. She was certain he would be musically inclined. She could thank Clyde for that. And she thanked her lucky stars that she'd given birth to her son. He was the joy of her life, her reason for rising in the morning, and lately, for putting one foot in front of the other.

Her smile faded. That was an awful lot to put on a little baby, she thought. It wouldn't always be this way, Maddie told herself. She wouldn't always feel such sharp pain when her mind wandered to Joshua. Soon she wouldn't think of him twenty-three of twenty-four hours a day. She wouldn't remember the way he'd held her and the way he'd made her feel, as if she were important, even vital. She wouldn't think about the crazy dreams she'd had about him.

Soon, she told herself. Soon.

The doorbell rang, interrupting her thoughts. Casting a quick glance at the clock, she wondered if it was Ben coming over to bum breakfast. Then she quickly put the baby down in his crib before heading to the door.

She opened the door to Joshua. The mere sight of him was enough of a surprise, but *roses?* She looked at the flowers, at him, then back at the flowers. She had to fight the urge to ask "Who died?" They couldn't be for her, she tried to tell herself, but no other logical reason for them came to mind. Her heart thumped faster.

Joshua narrowed his eyes. "What do you have in your hair?"

Maddie lifted her hand and felt her son's breakfast. "Rice cereal."

He gave a mock-perplexed look. "New beauty treatment?"

She shook her head. "You're so clever. Why are you here?"

His expression grew more intent. "To see you."

Her stomach took a quick dip, and Maddie bit back an oath. "To see me," she said skeptically. "Wearing rice cereal."

"Surely you're not surprised," he said, and walked past her into her house. Uninvited. "I've enjoyed seeing you with other foods on you. As a matter of fact I can recall seeing you wearing nothing but..." His voice trailed off as he flicked his gaze over her.

Whipped cream. Maddie's stomach took another dip as she closed the door behind him. For all her attempts at denial and forgetting, she knew she would never forget the whipped cream.

"These are for you." He offered the flowers to her.

Feeling a rush of pleasure and discomfort, she held the roses and smelled them. The first time she'd ever received flowers from a man. She didn't exactly know how to respond. "They're lovely," she said. "And unexpected. What possessed you?"

"A token of my affection." He said it with a straight face.

Her heart squeezed tight. "Thank you. Let me put them in water." She wheeled into the kitchen with Joshua following after her.

"I need to apologize," he said to her back.

Maddie nearly dropped the glass vase. The water running full force, she turned around and stared at him. "Excuse me?"

"I need to apologize. I hurt you. I didn't intend to."

Simple, but achingly sincere, his words cut straight to her heart. She took a deep breath. "I never thought you intended to hurt me. I just misread you." She turned the water off and tried to collect herself. ''I just realized we were headed in different directions.''

He cocked his head to one side. ''Do you really think that? That we're headed in different directions.''

Maddie blinked. ''Well, yes. I'm looking for something permanent. You aren't.'' She repeated the same words to herself three times.

''I think you may be wrong.''

''No,'' she said immediately. ''I'm not.''

''I think we'd both like to find out what we want with each other.'' He stepped closer and cupped her jaw. ''I think you still want to be with me.''

Maddie closed her eyes and groaned. ''When are you going to stop?''

He pulled her against him, and she felt his solid strength and arousal. Why did she feel as if she fit this man like a second skin? Why did her heart fight with her mind to get closer to him?

He ran his open mouth over her lips, tempting her, promising her. ''I'm not stopping until I get you,'' he told her, softening the punch of his sensual threat with his kiss.

Maddie kissed him back, and their caresses quickly grew out of control. He slid one of his hands up her shorts and with his other hand, guided her to touch him intimately.

We shouldn't do this. She heard it in her head, but had she said it aloud?

His fingers stroked her wet core. He rubbed her sensitive bead of pleasure, and she felt swollen inside and out. Needy for him. "Joshua," she said, knowing she should call a halt.

"Don't make me stop. You feel so good," he murmured. "You can blame it all on me," he said, and sucked her bottom lip into his mouth. "I need to feel you come apart in my hands."

That was all it took. His words and voice affected her like he was naked and inside her. She splintered, shattered, peaked. He made her shudder from her very depths until she slumped against him.

"Oh, Maddie, you're incredible. You're so beautiful. You have no idea how beautiful. You have no idea what you do to me," he told her, holding her tight.

Maddie's knees still trembled. She felt torn in two. It was as if her body knew she belonged to him, but her mind refused to allow it. "Oh, Joshua, this is craziness," she said breathlessly, and was mortified at the tears threatening behind her eyes. She swallowed over a lump in her throat.

Squeezing her eyes shut, she ducked her head against his chest. His strength, his heartbeat and scent were so familiar they felt as if they were a part of her. "I don't want to fool myself again," she told him. "When I'm with you, I feel a little out of control." She shook her head and made herself look up at him. "That's scary. I don't want to feel stupid for believing things might work out when they won't."

He paused a long moment, his gray eyes shifting like storm clouds. "Everyone's got their own doubts to tangle with," he finally said. "There's only one solution." His voice was firm, almost hard. "You've got to meet me halfway."

Maddie's throat tightened, because she feared Joshua's concept of meeting halfway would be like trying to leap across the Grand Canyon.

Twelve

A few nights later Joshua sat on Maddie's hill. Yes, he owned the property, but some crazy part of him had decided Maddie owned the hill. He thought about his life, his heart, and wondered if she owned more than the hill.

Joshua hadn't spent the past twelve years searching his soul about why Patrick's mother had died. He'd been too busy building his business and too clueless about raising a son on his own to do a lot of soul searching.

Lately, however, Joshua had done an awful lot of thinking, and some of it hadn't been enjoyable.

He wondered if, deep down, he had blamed himself for Gail's death. As a high school senior, he'd been the one to talk her into going all the way in his car. He'd been the one to forget about contraception.

She'd been the one to pay.

The unfairness upset him. Why'd she have to die? Why'd it have to go so terribly wrong? Why'd Patrick have to grow up without a mother?

The thoughts made his chest feel heavy with regret. He remembered walking around bearing this heaviness for years, but staying too busy to figure out the source of it. Now, he knew.

And the reason he knew was Maddie. She made the heaviness go away. She gave him hope. She made him feel the sunshine and taste the rain.

He craved her presence. She talked about being scared. He laughed without humor. If she knew how much he craved her, it would probably scare the living daylights out of her. It sure as hell disturbed him.

For so long it had been safe to stay uninvolved, to keep his heart and life locked away. It had been a relief not to dream or feel too much. Now, however, it was as if Maddie had shown him another world, and Joshua didn't want to leave. He smiled darkly to himself. No matter how hard she tried to push him away, he thought as he stared into the darkness, he wanted her.

A moment passed and he caught sight of Patrick walking toward him. From his seated position in the grass, Joshua was especially aware of Patrick's height. Where had the years gone? he wondered, but didn't voice the thought. Although Joshua hadn't met all his son's needs, he had the satisfaction of knowing he'd done his best, and Patrick had flourished. For his age he was a responsible, levelheaded kid. Worthy of his father's trust and respect.

When Joshua looked at Patrick, he thought maybe he hadn't screwed up too badly after all.

Patrick's gaze was curious. "You got a call from some Randolph woman. She says her mare's in season."

Joshua nodded. "She's early, but we can handle it."

Patrick shoved his hands in his pockets. "So, uh, what are you doin' up here?"

Joshua's lips tilted. He knew he was acting strange as hell. "Listening," he said. "Looking at the stars."

Patrick looked at him. "Oh." He looked up at the stars, then back to Joshua. "Does this have anything to do with Maddie?"

Joshua cocked his head to one side. His son had

good instincts. "Yeah. I've been thinking about Maddie some lately."

"Are you gonna marry her?"

His neck muscles tightened and he rubbed the back of it. "I haven't decided."

"Do you love her?"

Joshua paused a half beat. He wasn't exactly happy with the truth yet. "Yeah, I think I do."

"Do you think she loves you?"

Joshua's heart softened. "Yeah, I think she does, son." He looked into Patrick's searching gaze. "It takes more than love, sometimes."

Patrick shrugged as if he didn't understand. "Well, if you decide to marry her, I like having her around."

Joshua swallowed a grin. "Are you sure? What about Davey? Babies make a lot of noise."

Patrick shook his head. "He's an okay baby. Not too cranky. And he only throws up a little bit."

"That's true, but Maddie's a woman, and when they move into a house, they like to change things."

Patrick's eyes narrowed in wariness. "What kind of things?"

Joshua thought back to his earlier life. "Oh, they put perfume and makeup bottles all over the bathroom, and they like to put knickknacks around the house. They get upset when you leave socks on the floor, and like you to clean your room on a regular basis.''

Patrick was silent for a long moment. ''Since you've got a master bath, she'd probably put the perfume in your bathroom. The knickknacks are no big deal, but we might have to talk about cleaning my room.'' He gave a wily grin. ''Maybe for brownies.''

Joshua laughed. ''You've been taking lessons from Ben.''

''Ben's cool,'' Patrick said. ''Speaking of Ben, he-uh-let me drive his motorcycle.''

Joshua raised his eyebrows. Patrick knew Joshua didn't like the idea of him driving a motorcycle yet. ''He did?''

''Yeah. I was supercareful,'' he rushed to say. ''I wore a helmet and didn't drive too fast or anything. I've got another computer class after school tomorrow, and I was hoping you would let me drive the motorcycle to school.''

Joshua's automatic response was no, but then he saw the undiluted hope on his son's face. Patrick was a good kid. Worthy of trust. He took a deep breath. ''This won't be a regular occurrence,'' he said, ''and—''

''Al-l-l-l-l-right!'' Patrick yelled. ''Dad, you won't regret this. I'll be so careful.''

"You damn well better be." Joshua stood. "Wear the helmet."

"I will."

"And you drive defensively, because people don't see motorcycles as easily as they see cars."

"I know."

"Keep your distance and no showing off," Joshua continued. "Even if the girls are watching."

Patrick just grinned. "I won't."

Joshua made it inside his front door just as Maddie whirled from the kitchen. Her eyes flew open wide in surprise. She'd obviously finagled a key from Patrick, and the little scamp was trying to sneak away without seeing him.

"In a rush again?" he asked mildly, leaning against the door.

She straightened her posture. "Not a tremendous hurry," Maddie said. "I understand you've been busy with settling and breeding and studding and stuff...." She waved her hands. "So I didn't want to interrupt your schedule."

Why not? Joshua thought. You've interrupted everything else. He lifted an eyebrow. "Studding?"

"Well, whatever it is that you do, or your horses

do. You said something about settling and studs, so—''

He chuckled. ''Close enough.''

''Has all of that been going well? The mares are cooperative and the studs are—'' She shrugged.

''The studs are always ready,'' Joshua told her, thinking how much the animal kingdom mirrored human mating rituals. ''We don't usually have much problem with the mares unless someone has messed up with the calculations and testing and they're not in season.''

She nodded. ''And how do you know if it—'' She searched for the word. ''Takes?''

''The stick turns blue,'' he said wryly.

''Oh.'' She twined her hands together. ''I don't know much about horses. I rode a pony a couple of times when I was a kid.''

Confused, Joshua studied her. It had looked as if she was trying to avoid him again, but she wasn't bolting for the door right now. ''Would you like to ride?''

''The stud?''

''No,'' Joshua said flatly, immediately. ''He's mean, ornery, and the only thing he's good for is f—'' He broke off to find a gentler term. ''Settling mares. I have a real sweet older mare who would give you a nice ride.''

She tilted her head to one side and smiled. ''Is

this your way of saying you don't think I can handle a stud?''

Joshua felt his blood began to heat. He would almost think she was flirting with him. ''I know you can't handle my stud. My horse. But that's not to say I wouldn't want you handling anything of mine.''

Her gaze met his. ''Is that an invitation?''

The look in her eyes made him want to howl like a wild animal. ''Yes,'' he said. ''What do you think of that?''

She moved closer, close enough to touch. ''I'm... thinking.'' She lifted her lips to his, and Joshua felt his heart pound against his rib cage. She felt so warm, so soft, so alive, so good, he would swear he heard bells.

''The phone's ringing,'' Maddie managed to say when she pulled back slightly.

He sucked in a deep breath and swore. Hell, he was so aroused he could have taken her against the wall. He debated answering the phone, then remembered he was waiting on a call about another stud he wanted to buy. ''Just a minute,'' he said firmly. ''Don't go anywhere.''

He jogged to the kitchen and idly noticed the table set for three. Perhaps Maddie hadn't intended to cut and run after all. He picked up the phone. ''Blackwell,'' he said.

"Mr. Blackwell, are you Patrick Blackwell's father?" a woman asked.

"Yes," he said, frowning a little. He never got calls about Patrick.

"I'm calling from Roanoke Memorial Hospital, and your son has been in a serious automobile accident. He has arrived in the emergency room and is being examined for treatment. May we have phone permission to treat your child?"

His blood turned to ice. "Patrick?"

"Yes, sir. May we have phone permission to treat your child?"

"How serious?"

"I'm not certain. He is being evaluated. May we have phone permission to treat your child?"

"How bad is it?"

"I'm sorry, Mr. Blackwell, but I'm not certain. He is being evaluated right now. May we have phone permission to treat your child so we can begin X rays and lab work?"

"Yes," he said, frustrated when he realized she wasn't going to disclose further information. He felt Maddie's gaze on him. "Tell him I'll be there as soon as I can." He placed the phone into the cradle, fighting a terrible, terrible fear.

"What is it?" Maddie asked.

He shook his head. "It was that motorcycle," he muttered to himself as he headed for the door.

"That damn motorcycle. I knew I shouldn't have let him drive it. I should have gotten rid of it. It's pure temptation for a teenage boy."

He felt her take his arm. "Joshua, what happened?" she demanded.

"It's Patrick. He's in the emergency room. I've gotta go."

"Oh, no." She paused barely a heartbeat. "Well, I'm going, too."

His mind moving a mile a minute, Joshua shook his head. "I don't know how long this will take. Don't know his condition. She mentioned X-rays. That means he's probably broken something. A motorcycle accident can be messy," he said, and felt a slice of pain at the scenarios running through his head.

Grabbing her purse, she looked at him incredulously. "I'm coming with you."

Something inside him resisted the idea, although he couldn't say why. His mind was on Patrick. "What about Davey?"

"I'll call Jenna Jean or Ben from the hospital. Do you want me to drive?"

She was serious, he thought, as they both ran to his truck. He almost laughed, but thoughts of Patrick prevented him. "I don't have time to stop for a trooper if you get a ticket."

Maddie sighed. "Good point."

During the drive, in some corner of his mind, he noticed the way Maddie tried to reassure him. She touched his arm, asked a few questions that required one-word answers and said, "I think he'll be okay."

Joshua wondered and worried. Something inside him wouldn't allow him to accept her comfort. He'd had too much practice handling tragedy alone. After he checked emergency registration, a nurse's aide led him into a separate room. His throat tightened with each passing second until the doctor arrived.

"Concussion," the doctor said. "His leg is broken in two places, and he needs sutures. According to the police, the accident wasn't his fault. He tried to avoid it."

Joshua's gut twisted viciously, and he stiffened. He shouldn't have allowed Patrick to drive the motorcycle. "Is he conscious?"

"For the most part," the doctor said. "He's still a little confused. He keeps telling the nurses he tried to get out of the way."

"He's such a good kid," Maddie said, and gently squeezed his arm. Comfort, he thought, and was almost lulled into turning to her. But Joshua turned away instead. He couldn't accept comfort while his son was in pain.

"Yeah, he is," Joshua said. "I want to see him."

"He hasn't been cleaned up," the doctor said.

"I want to see him." He looked at Maddie. "If you need to go home..."

Maddie shook her head. "I'll wait. Can you let me know how he is?"

"Yeah." He nodded as he moved away. It was peculiar as hell, but he felt a sense of loss as soon as he'd taken three steps. The feeling confused him, but he didn't have time to think about it. "I'll let you know as soon as I can."

Joshua knew it was every parent's nightmare to see their child bleeding and in pain in the emergency room. When he saw Patrick, however, he felt as if his heart was ripped out of his chest. He had to grit his teeth together to block his emotions.

Patrick looked up at him like he was drowning. "Dad. I swear it wasn't my fault. I tried to—"

Joshua shook his head and squeezed Patrick's shoulder. "Hush. I know you did your best. Let's concentrate on getting you taken care of."

He didn't stray from Patrick's side through the stitches or when they set his leg. He sent a nurse out to tell Maddie the status, but it was hours before Patrick was taken to a room.

With his son asleep, Joshua walked into the

waiting room to grab some coffee. He was surprised to find Maddie still there.

She rose to her feet as soon as she saw him. "How is he?"

He rolled his shoulders. "He's gonna be okay. That broken leg won't be a cakewalk, but he's gonna be okay."

Maddie sensed the easing of tension in Joshua. "What can I do for you? Is there something you need done at your house, or can I get you some food, or—"

He shook his head. "Nothing. I'm okay. I made a call to one of the men who works for me, and he'll cover everything. You should go home. You shouldn't have spent the night in the waiting room."

Feeling superfluous, she studied him. He seemed distant to her. "You've had a long night," she said softly.

He shrugged. "I've had a lot of practice getting through long nights."

But you didn't have to go it alone, this time. She brushed the thought away, but it persisted. "Are you sure I can't do anything?"

"Let me give you a ride home."

She shook her head. "No, Ben kept Davey for me. He called a couple of times asking about Patrick, and he told me he would come and get me."

He raked a hand through his hair. "Are you sure?"

"Sure," she said, reaching her arms around him, but he felt stiff and remote. "You can relax," she whispered. "A hug isn't supposed to hurt."

He gave her a quick squeeze, then backed away, and his gaze seemed to go right through her.

"I'll check on you later," she said.

He gave a noncommittal nod and walked down the hall.

Maddie watched him, relieved that Patrick would be okay, but concerned about Joshua. His distant response troubled her.

She phoned Ben, and he took her home. During the drive, after she filled him in on Patrick, she brooded over Joshua's behavior.

"Mad, you're making me nervous. You haven't been this quiet since you found out you were pregnant." Ben paused and grimaced. "You're not pregnant again, are you?"

She rolled her eyes. "No. I'm not pregnant. I was thinking about Joshua and how aloof he seemed last night and today." She frowned in concentration. "I know he was very worried about Patrick, but he seemed to close in on himself."

"Joshua is a major league loner. He's used to coping on his own."

She glanced at Ben. "I agree, but what makes

you say that? He hasn't allowed women into his life for several years, but he's always had Patrick.''

"All the more reason for him to stand alone. He's probably so used to putting out fires on his own, he doesn't know what to do with another human, let alone a woman.''

Maddie could argue the issue of whether or not Joshua knew what to do with a woman, but perhaps Ben had a point. "You're saying he's dealt with crises on his own so much, that he doesn't know how to share them.''

Ben nodded as he pulled into her driveway. "Yep," he said. "And I bet Joshua's not the type to ever learn.''

The thought didn't comfort Maddie. Since he had told her to meet him halfway, Maddie had taken another turn and opened herself to him again. She scowled at herself. Who was she fooling? When had she successfully shut him out?

But now she needed to take a hard look at his behavior. What if he shut her out? She already knew he would stand by her during a crisis of hers. But would she be able to accept him keeping her at arm's length during his rough moments?

She shook her head. Even with all the changes she'd been through in the past year, Maddie knew she was not a woman for half measures. Although she might be more careful now, she would never be prudent. She had a go-for-it quality, and it had been responsible for her triumphs and losses.

She wondered, when all was said and done, which way it would end with Joshua.

Thirteen

Joshua pulled his front door shut behind him and leaned against it. Not bothering to turn on a light, he just stood in the silent darkness and sighed. The doctor said he wanted to keep Patrick for observation one more night. Everyone, including Patrick, had told Joshua to go home.

So, here he was, forced to face the absence of the noisiness and frantic pace of the hospital. At the hospital there were a hundred interruptions. Take the blood pressure, check his sutures, take his temperature, give him lunch… On and on it went. The routine had offered little peace, but it at least had kept the demons at bay.

It had kept him from wondering if he'd failed Patrick by allowing him to ride the motorcycle. It had kept him from memories of Gail's repeated stays at the hospital, and that last trip to the emergency room when nothing could be done. It had almost kept him from missing Maddie.

"Another long day," a soft feminine voice murmured from the other side of the room. "No rest for the wicked."

Joshua's eyes flew open. It was Maddie. He couldn't distinguish much more than the shape of her because of the darkness of the room. "Where are you?"

"Coming closer," she said, walking toward him. She pressed a glass into his hand and he breathed in her scent. "Drink up. How's Patrick?"

He automatically swallowed the wine. It was cool and pleasantly dry. "Patrick will be okay. The good news is the motorcycle was totaled," he said. "So the temptation will be removed."

"Maybe," she said. "Have you had dinner?"

He concentrated. "I think. Yeah, I had a couple of burgers." Watching her eyes glint in the darkness, he took a few more gulps and the wine was gone. "What are you doing here?"

"Checking on you." She took the glass. "Let me get you more wine."

"I'll turn on the light," he said.

"No," she said immediately. "Take a seat on the sofa and relax."

Why? he thought about asking, but his weariness won and he slumped onto the sofa. He watched Maddie return and accepted the refilled wineglass as she sat beside him.

"On a scale of one to ten, how terrified were you when you got the call yesterday?" she ventured.

Still tense, Joshua rolled his shoulders. "Twenty."

"And when Joshua Blackwell handles a crisis, he does it alone."

He met her gaze. "It's the only way I know."

"No hugs, no comfort, no sharing," she continued, sliding closer to him.

He inhaled deeply, still waiting for the tight feeling in his chest to loosen. "I can't remember having any of that."

She put her hand on his arm and rubbed her mouth on his cheek. "Then maybe it's time for you to make some new memories."

She took his wineglass and reached across him to set it on the end table. She felt warm and smelled of a sweet, alluring perfume. "Maybe it's time for you to learn a new way," she said, and kissed him.

His chest finally expanded, but other parts of his

body tightened. Her mouth was sweet and ardent, her hands both soothing and seductive. He breathed deeply, wanting to inhale her, absorb her. Then, he sensed, all would be right. It wasn't that he couldn't survive without her, he told himself. It was that he didn't want to be without her.

He felt her fingers unfasten the buttons of his shirt. "What are you doing to me, Maddie?"

Her lips lifted in a she-cat smile. "It's a surprise."

His gut twisted, and his pulse pounded in all his pleasure points. Before he could say anything else, she slid her hand over his chest and gave him a French kiss that sent his body temperature soaring.

He thought about asking his question again, but what she was doing felt so damn good, he decided to hang on for the ride. She was moving more than his body. Joshua had never felt so cherished and turned on at the same time. He hadn't known it was possible.

She lowered her mouth to his chest and her hand to his belt. As she skimmed her lips down his chest to his belly, he swelled beneath the very suggestion of her touch. In achingly slow movements, she unfastened his belt and lowered his zipper.

When her hand slipped beneath his briefs to his hardness, he groaned. "Oh, Maddie," he muttered.

She swirled her tongue around his belly button,

then dipped it inside, and he groaned again. Her mouth was so warm and sweet he didn't want her to stop.

Draped across his thighs, she stroked him intimately with her fingers, cupping him. He was hard, throbbing, ready to climb the walls from her teasing touch.

She lowered her mouth still farther and paused. Joshua held his breath. Would she? A second passed and she took him into her mouth.

"Ah, Maddie." Joshua clenched his eyes shut at the incredible pleasure. He felt the flick of her tongue over his swollen masculinity and began to swear under his breath.

He gradually opened his eyes, and the sight of her with her lips caressing him intimately nearly sent him over the edge. Her hair whispered over his thighs and abdomen, and her hands stroked his skin. It was too erotic for words, but Maddie was doing more than making love to him, she was laying claim to his heart and mind.

His resistance and doubt slid from his grip. She was tenderly taking him past the point of return. Perspiration beaded on the back of his neck. He wove his fingers through her hair as she pushed him further and further.

He could barely breathe, and his entire body trembled from intense arousal. His heart was too full, the pleasure too much. Calling her name, he burst over the edge, falling, falling, until she caught him.

Taking deep breaths, he drew her tightly against him. Every other breath, he swore, or said her name. She kissed his neck and cheek.

Finally he collected himself enough to see straight, although he wouldn't have put money on being able to walk. He stared at her in the darkness. "You are incredible. Hell, what—" He shook his head and released a long breath. "What was that for?"

She curled against him. "There are lots of different ways to handle a crisis. You're used to doing it one way, all alone. I wanted to show you another way." Lifting her head, she brushed her hand against his hair. "There are lots of ways to be together in a crisis when you're with someone you love."

His heart swelled again in his chest and he kissed her. He wondered when he'd been more loved. He wondered when someone had given to him so unselfishly.

"I love you," she whispered. "You need to know that." Her eyes darkened with emotion and she took a breath. "You need to know something else, too. I'm not a fifty-fifty kind of woman," she said, her voice stronger as she sat away from him.

"Not the halfway kind, either. When it comes to love, I don't do fractions. I give all of me." Her gaze boldly met his. "And I want all of you."

He watched in amazement as she stood. "Deal with it, Joshua. I love you."

Still reeling from her lovemaking and her words, he watched her walk out the door. *Out the door?* Who did this woman think she was? He pulled himself together and rose none-too-steadily to his feet. His damn knees were still weak, but he ran to the porch and caught her as she rounded the side of his house to where she must have hidden her car.

"Where in hell do you think you're going?" he demanded.

She gave him a double take. "Home. I thought you might need a little rest."

"After you rendered me nearly unable to walk?"

She blinked. "Are you complaining?"

"About you leaving, I am."

She paused. "Oh," she said, searching his gaze. "Well, reality bites. I don't have an overnight baby-sitter tonight, so I need to go home."

He took a deep breath and pulled her against him. "Maddie, you can't make love to me like that and just walk out."

"I thought women had more of a problem with that than men."

He shrugged. "I don't know about that. All I know is I want you to stay." He swallowed. "I want you to stay forever."

Amazement shining in her eyes, she looked up at him. "Forever?"

He twined his fingers through hers. "I want to put a ring on your finger and make promises that I will keep. I love you, Maddie, and I want to love you for the rest of my life."

Then Maddie started crying and got his shirt wet, but Joshua didn't mind because he knew it was right. He would never spend a night without dreams or Maddie again.

Two months later they were married on her hill. It rained a little, but the sun came out and Maddie felt like that was pretty much what had happened throughout her life. It often rained, but the sun eventually came out. With Joshua, she finally felt as if she'd found a place where she fit. A place designed for her.

Her heart was too full to contain it all, and he gently teased her as she struggled with her tears. But it was an incredible day. Her two best friends in the world were beside her. Her brother and Patrick, who was healing quickly, stood by Joshua.

The surprise that tipped it over the edge for her, though, was her father escorting her to the outdoor altar and her mother's appearance.

Without her knowledge, Joshua had visited her parents and helped them to see her in a different light. Now Davey would know his grandparents.

She made the vows and felt each one in her heart. When Joshua repeated his, she could see in his honest gray eyes that he would always love her. The wonder of it still took her breath.

He held her tight and kissed her. Then, after pictures, they led the caravan to a lovely small inn for the reception.

"Did you mind the rain?" she asked him.

Joshua shook his head and grinned at her. "No, I've gotten so I kinda like the rain."

"It wrecked my hair," she grumbled. "And I ripped the bottom of my dress when I got out of the car."

He kissed her on the nose. "You look beautiful."

"You look spotless," she accused.

"Time to cut the cake," Ben said, with Patrick by his side. "Save the mushy stuff for later and feed us now."

"It's always your stomach. You're so primitive," Maddie said.

He shrugged. "It makes me easy to bribe."

"He's got a point," Joshua said, walking with her to the table that displayed the three-tier devil's food cake with chocolate icing.

Maddie sliced two pieces and smiled for the camera. Then, in keeping with tradition, Joshua served her a bite from his hand. She licked his fingers and grinned at his surprise.

She took her turn and lifted the piece to his mouth. "Maddie," the photographer called. "Look this way."

She swiveled her head, and her hand swerved. She heard a collective gasp and jerked back around. She'd rubbed the devil's food cake against Joshua's crisp, perfectly white tuxedo shirt.

"Oops." She winced at him. "Is this when I say you looked a little too perfect, anyway?"

He glanced down at his shirt and chuckled. "I thought you would at least wait until we got to our suite before you started eating things off me."

Maddie threw him a look of mock censure. "You have a dirty mind."

His gaze grew sensual and he drew her closer. "I learned from the best." The applause from the wedding guests faded from her consciousness as Joshua kissed her.

Later that night, after the toasts had been made and the rice had been thrown, Maddie sprayed herself with perfume and pulled on the negligee her friend Emily had given her. She glanced down at the golden band and diamond ring on her third finger. When he'd given her the diamond, Joshua had told her it was a star he'd pulled from the sky. She'd cried.

Now she was married. To Joshua.

Her heart squeezed tight, and she took a deep breath. She wanted tonight to be special. Jenna Jean was taking care of Davey, so Maddie could focus her undivided attention on her husband. She would tell him again how wonderful he was, and how much she loved him. Then she would show him.

She glanced in the mirror and saw a happy, happy woman. She hoped she could help make him just as happy. Opening the door, she walked out of the bathroom into the lushly decorated suite. The only light came from the bathroom. Joshua had turned out the rest of them. She curled her toes into the plush carpet and turned to find him on the bed.

She dropped her jaw at the sight of him. He was wearing nothing but a guitar. "Well, hello," she said, walking toward him. "What is this all about?"

He looked amused, but resigned. "You once

told me you always were a sucker for a guy and a guitar.''

She smiled. "So you bought a guitar?"

"I felt like I had to. And I learned a song."

Amazed, she put her hand to her chest and felt her eyes swell with tears. "For me? You learned a song for me."

Joshua held up his hand. "Don't get too excited. It's just one song. One very simple song."

"Play it! Play it!"

"Okay," he said, and placed his fingers on the strings. With intense concentration he started to play, and despite the fact that it wasn't an electric guitar, Maddie could clearly make out the well-known three-chord melody of "Louie, Louie."

She laughed and cried and threw her arms around him. Maddie Palmer Blackwell had gotten caught again. This time for good.

* * * * *

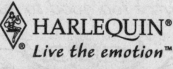

Harlequin Historicals®
Historical Romantic Adventure!

From rugged lawmen and valiant knights to defiant heiresses and spirited frontierswomen, Harlequin Historicals will capture your imagination with their dramatic scope, passion and adventure.

Harlequin Historicals . . . they're too good to miss!

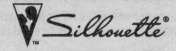

THE
POCKET G
TO
Mischie
BART KING

THE POCKET GUIDE TO

TO

Mischief

BART KING

Illustrations by Brenda Brown

Gibbs Smith, Publisher

TO ENRICH AND INSPIRE HUMANKIND

Salt Lake City | Charleston | Santa Fe | Santa Barbara

First Edition
12 11 10 09   5 4 3

This book makes mention of some activities that theo-
retically could carry an element of risk. Readers
assume all legal responsibility for their actions.

Please contact the author at kingbart@comcast.net.

Published by
Gibbs Smith, Publisher
P.O. Box 667
Layton, Utah 84041
Orders: 1.800.835.4993
www.gibbs-smith.com

Designed by Michel Vrána, Black Eye Design
Printed and bound in Canada

Library of Congress Cataloging-in-Publication Data
King, Bart, 1962-
  The pocket guide to mischief / Bart King ; illustrations
  by Brenda Brown. — 1st ed.
     p. cm.
  Includes bibliographical references.
  ISBN-13: 978-1-4236-0366-5
  ISBN-10: 1-4236-0366-4
  1. Practical jokes—Humor. 2. Conduct of life—Humor.
  I. Title.
  PN6231.P67K56 2008
  818'.602—dc22
                                        2007037105

*This book is dedicated
to my Nemesis.*

★★★

*Think of this as a preview
of coming attractions.*

CONTENTS

★★★

Warning!

Do not be misled by this book's cover. A mistake was made at the printing press, and apparently this book, which is about the importance of nutrition and dental hygiene, got mixed up with someone's book about mischief.

So turn the page and enjoy learning about how to enjoy a wholesome and healthy lifestyle.

Introduction

*"LET THEM CALL IT MISCHIEF: WHEN IT
IS PAST AND PROSPERED IT WILL BE
VIRTUE."* —Ben Jonson

If you've made it this far, you must be
feeling *really* good. Medical experts
believe that making and escaping
mischief (like that fake introduction) is
quite good for a person's health. In fact,
if you follow this book's advice, you'll live
to be eighty years old.[1]

---

1. This is a *footnote*. Mischief makers use footnotes
a lot because it forces the reader to look all the way
down here. Ha ha!

I'm almost a doctor, and I want you to know that I'm glad you have made such a healthy choice. I'm also proud of you for having the courage to pick up this book in the first place. After all, some people think that mischief is always bad, pranks are always mean, and troublemaking is always wrong.

BUT MISCHIEF MAKERS ACTUALLY PROVIDE A VALUABLE SERVICE TO THE REST OF SOCIETY. THINK ABOUT HOW BORING LIFE WOULD BE IF EVERYONE WERE A PERFECT SAINT ALL THE TIME! MISCHIEF MAKERS GIVE THE REST OF US A GOOD LAUGH AND FUNNY STORIES TO TELL TO EACH OTHER.

Maybe you're already a mischief maker. If so, good for you! Believe it or not, we make the world a better place. We are our nation's unsung heroes!

What is it that makes a great mischief maker? Being clever is good. After all, it's hard to be a smart aleck if you're not actually smart to begin with. (Stupid alecks are a lot less impressive.) And of

11

course, you need to be willing to make trouble on a small, amusing, and non-destructive scale.

AND DON'T WORRY IF YOU ARE CURRENTLY A DO-GOODER . . . GAG, RETCH, VOMIT . . . THIS BOOK CAN HELP! EVEN IF YOU DON'T THINK YOU HAVE WHAT IT TAKES TO MAKE MISCHIEF AND MAYHEM, TRUST ME: THERE IS ALREADY A MISCHIEF MAKER INSIDE YOU.

You see, your body is composed of incredibly tiny bits of matter called atoms. These are so small that it takes almost a million atoms to be as wide as one hair. Since atoms last practically forever, all the atoms currently inside you used to belong to something—or someone—else.

Some of the atoms inside you came from stars, some from rocks, and some even came from people long ago. Scientists agree that every living person has a few atoms inside that were once part of every single other person who ever lived on the planet. This would include charming folks like Vlad the Impaler (1431–1476) and Gertrude the Booger Flicker (600–678).

So you see, you do have a little bit of a mischief maker inside you after all. Everyone does!

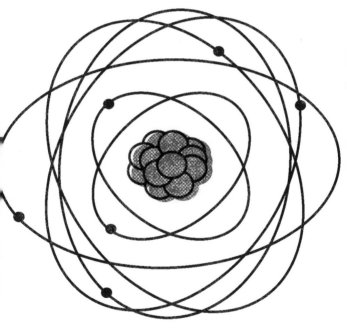

The Atom

Before we move on, you have to agree to the following rules. (If you don't, this book will now give you a small electric shock.) Of course, following the rules goes against everything that a mischief maker stands for. We live to break the rules. (Bending the rules is also okay. If you can't do that, at least try to leave dirty handprints on them.) So the first rule of mischief making is not to have any rules.

AND I'M NOW GOING TO BREAK THAT RULE. RAISE YOUR MIDDLE HAND AND REPEAT AFTER ME:

RULES
for Pranking, Hoaxing, Shenanigans, and General Mischief Making

1. I WILL BE SAFE.

So set that beehive down. Now walk away slowly. Okay, run!

2. I WILL NOT DAMAGE OR DESTROY PROPERTY.

So put down that thermonuclear device. Walk away slowly. Okay, run, and keep going until you're 1,200 miles away.

3. I WILL BE SLY.

Since the key to pulling off a prank is to not get caught, don't set off anyone's prank-dar. So try not to get caught!

4. I WILL NEVER HURT ANYONE WITH A PRANK.

Sure, you might want to trick people and have a laugh. But your trick should be so clever that instead of making your victim look stupid, he or she enjoys it as much as you did.

5. I WILL NEVER PRANK ANYONE FOR MONEY.

Unless someone offers you some. In which case you should take it with an evil chuckle while rubbing your palms together.

Now shove a fist into the air and yell,

"Hail, cheese whiz!"

Okay, I guess you're ready to turn the page.

17

Choosing

YOUR TARGET OR NEMESIS

*"BANISH TOMORROW! YOUR NEMESIS
LAYS WAIT."* —*Antiphilus of Byzantium*

It's important for a beginning mischief
maker like yourself to narrow your focus
to one person. This will help you with
your technique, and everyone else you
know will be grateful. I will call the lucky
person you select your Nemesis.

Your Nemesis is your foe, your opponent,
your archenemy, and your ambition. He
or she might be related to you or be your
best friend. Because of this, you will be

careful not to go too far with your mischief making. After all, you and your Nemesis have a relationship! Plus, you don't want to give your Nemesis any reason to throw ninja stars at you or try to run you over with a dump truck.

Of course, your Nemesis does not have to be a person. It could be something slightly larger, like a city or even North America. But it is not very easy to play a good practical joke on a continent. Often, your prank will turn into an *impractical* joke, which is not as satisfying to carry out.

A STRANGER CANNOT BE A NEMESIS. NOR CAN IT BE ANYONE WHO IS SUPERSENSITIVE OR SHY.

In addition, your Nemesis should be someone who is at least your age, size, and "popularity." In other words, make sure your Nemesis is at your social position or higher.[1]

---

1. As males seem to tease each other more than females, some people feel that males might make better Nemesises . . . ses.

Avoid selecting anyone with lots of tattoos or a nunchuck collection. And unless you have training in sword fighting, do not pick a Nemesis who might challenge you to a duel after one of your fun-loving pranks. In my experience, pain hurts, and it's hard to get bloodstains out of most clothes. Oh, and never play a prank on the Queen of England. She has a trained champion whose job is to challenge anyone who messes with her. Really.

After giving the choice so much thought, you probably picked someone who is also a mischief maker to be your Nemesis. Perfect!

AS NICCOLÒ MACHIAVELLI WROTE IN 1513, "IT IS DOUBLE PLEASURE TO DECEIVE THE DECEIVER."

And if you pick your Nemesis wisely, you will benefit society and make the world a better place. That's because the sensitive, shy people will be inspired by your excellent role modeling and start

Quick Mischief

★ Put a sprinkler under someone's chair at a picnic, and turn it on at just the right moment.
★ Peel the labels off all the canned goods in the house.
★ Stitch closed someone's shirt sleeve or pant leg.

to come out of their shells. Once they do this, you'll have more people you can play practical jokes on. It's a beautiful system!

ONE LAST THING! Don't tell your Nemesis that he or she is your Nemesis. That will only make the Nemesis suspicious of you! Instead, consider getting your Nemesis some flowers. Allow me to suggest a nice bouquet of *Rafflesia arnoldi*. Known as the largest flower on the planet, it is also known as the "corpse flower." That's because the corpse flower's bloom gives off the smell of rotting meat. It's the perfect gift for that not-so-special someone!

Corpse Flower

Mischief Quiz!

Answering these questions will give you a better idea of who you are. And besides learning to not eat a lot of soup before riding on a roller coaster, isn't that one of the most important things anyone could find out? So sharpen your pencil, put your thinking cap on inside-out, and pull up your socks. It's test time!

1. WALKING ALONG THE BEACH, YOU SEE TWO CHILDREN BUILDING A SAND CASTLE. YOU . . .

a. Introduce yourself and offer to help dig the moat and swat away errant volleyballs.
b. Introduce yourself as "King Sandy" and spend the rest of the day constructing a huge sandcastle with a working drawbridge right next to theirs.
c. Shout, "Viking attack!" and run through their castle.

2. YOU GET HOME AND ARE LOOKING TO RELAX. YOU ARE MOST LIKELY TO . . .

a. Gather the neighborhood kids together to put on a play for senior citizens.
b. Open this book and take notes.
c. Gather the neighborhood kids together to organize a fund-raiser for you.

3. *YOU WATCH AS A NEIGHBOR WALKS HIS DOG PAST YOUR HOUSE. THE DOG BUSTS A GRUMPY, LEAVING A HUGE PILE OF POOP IN YOUR YARD. THE NEIGHBOR THEN WALKS OFF WITHOUT PICKING IT UP. YOU . . .*

a. Go clean it up.
b. Put it in an Easter basket and leave it on the neighbor's porch.
c. What you do is so horrible, I can't write it. Let's just say it involves dog poop, a spatula, and a slingshot.

4. *SPLAT! YOUR NEMESIS HAS JUST THROWN A WATER BALLOON AT YOU. YOUR FIRST RESPONSE IS TO . . .*

a. Say, "Ha ha! Good one!"
b. Begin making plans for a water *blimp* to destroy your Nemesis with.
c. Sharpen your bayonet collection while muttering, "Vengeance."

(continued on next page)

5. *YOU'RE A GIRL. (IF YOU ARE NOT REALLY A GIRL, PRETEND. IF YOU ARE A GIRL, CONTINUE BEING ONE.) A GUY YOU DON'T LIKE MUCH ASKS, "WHAT WOULD IT TAKE FOR ME TO BECOME YOUR BOYFRIEND?" YOUR RESPONSE:*

a. "You're very nice, but I'm afraid it's just not possible."
b. "If every other guy in town got leprosy, I'd consider it."
c. Would include laughter and pointing.

6. *YOU JUST BOUGHT SOME SOCKS. THE CLERK SAYS, "CAN I HELP YOU WITH ANYTHING ELSE?" YOU SAY:*

a. "No, thank you."
b. "Well, I do have a rash on my arm that's been itching like crazy."
c. "Are you saying I need help?"

(look, even more quiz on page 27)

7. *YOUR BLOOD TYPE IS:*

a. B *positive*!
b. B negative
c. O I'm going to knock you into next week

8. *YOUR IDEAL JOB WOULD BE ONE WHERE YOU COULD . . .*

a. Feed the hungry and clothe the . . . people who need clothes.
b. Write books like this.
c. Release starving leopards into the petting zoo.

9. *YOU SEE YOUR MEAN NEIGHBOR THROW A ROCK AT A SQUIRREL. YOU DECIDE TO . . .*

a. Give the squirrel a nut the size of a cantaloupe to make up for it.
b. Call your neighbor from a public

(continued on next page)

phone and tell him that you're calling
from the zoo about an escaped wolf
that is prowling his neighborhood.
c. Release starving leopards into his
   kitchen.

10. *YOU'RE AT THE "15 ITEMS OR LESS" LINE AT THE
    SUPERMARKET, AND THE PERSON IN FRONT OF
    YOU HAS A SHOPPING CART STUFFED WITH ITEMS.
    YOU . . .*

a. Smile pleasantly at the clerk and roll
   your eyes.
b. Count loudly as each item goes on
   the conveyer belt: "18! 19! 20!"
c. Lay on the conveyer belt in protest.

11. *YOU SEE A POORLY PARKED CAR THAT NEEDS TO
    BE WASHED. YOU . . .*

a. Walk past it, whistling happily.
b. Look around to make sure you're alone,

(continued on next page)

and then you use your finger to write "I am old and dirty" on the window.

c. Hijack a tow truck, tow the car, and leave it in a large body of water.

12. YOU ACCIDENTALLY BELCH WHILE EATING IN A CROWDED RESTAURANT. YOU . . .

a. Apologize to everyone in the restaurant. Then you leave a big tip and quietly exit.

b. Tell everyone, "In many cultures, that's how you say it was a good meal. Too bad this isn't one of them!"

c. Lean forward, saying, "That belch perfectly covered the sound of me farting."

Scores:

IF YOU ANSWERED MOSTLY A:

You are an *innocent do-gooder*. Also

(continued on next page)

known as *goody two-shoes, sweetie three-socks*, and *smiley guy one-sweater*. Read this book. It will help you.

IF YOU ANSWERED MOSTLY B:

You are a *mischief maker*, aka *wisenheimer, prankster, wise guy, wise-acre,* or *hoaxster*. But whatever they call you, you're the tops! Congratulations, and enjoy the rest of the book![1]

IF YOU ANSWERED MOSTLY C:

You are a *mook*, otherwise known as an *ogre, goon, scalawag,* or *juvenile delinquent*. Some people might call you violent or antisocial, but not to your face, of course. After you finish reading this book, consider a career in dentistry or school counseling.

---

1. If you just missed out on being in this category, you may be a *noodj,* the most innocent, harmless type of mischief maker. Read this book for tips on how to be more ambitious.

Harmless Trickery 101

HOW TO DEFEND HOME AND SELF

"NOW, LET IT WORK: MISCHIEF, THOU ART AFOOT,
TAKE THOU WHAT COURSE THOU WILT!"
—William Shakespeare

Maybe you're wondering if you should still be reading this book. Are you thinking that you might get in trouble because of it? Don't worry! The only way to avoid getting in trouble in life is to do nothing and say nothing. But if nothing is the safe road, it's also a pretty crummy one. Besides, if you follow my advice, everything will work out perfectly!

31

For instance, let's talk about pranks. It's important to note that pranks have nothing to do with hazing, harassing, or hurting people. Are you kidding? We're here to have fun and make the world a better place. To help define what pranks are, a famous mischief maker named Abbie Hoffman divided them into three different categories:

1. PRANKS THAT MAKE FUN OF SOMEONE WHO IS POWERFUL, LIKE THE LEADER OF A COUNTRY OR THE MEAN LADY DOWN THE STREET WHO THROWS PEACH PITS AT YOU. MISCHIEF THAT MOCKS THE POWERFUL IS CALLED "SATIRE." IT IS SOMETIMES WITTY, SOMETIMES BRAVE, AND IS OFTEN TRYING TO MAKE A POINT.

2. PRANKS THAT ARE SILLY. THESE KINDS OF PRANKS CAN BE SO WEIRD THAT THEY'RE FUNNY, AND THEY DON'T ALWAYS NEED A "VICTIM." (THERE ARE A LOT OF PRANKS LIKE THIS IN HERE.)

3. PRANKS THAT ARE JUST PLAIN MEAN. AS YOU KNOW, MEAN PEOPLE STINK.

Now here's an amazing fact: It is impossible to flush a ping-pong ball down the toilet. That's because a ping-pong ball is so light and airy, it just never goes down the drain.

TO TEST YOUR KNOWLEDGE OF PRANKS, WHICH OF ABBIE HOFFMAN'S CATEGORIES ABOVE WOULD "TRYING TO FLUSH A PING-PONG BALL" FALL UNDER?

a. Trying to flush a ping-pong ball is satire, because you are mocking the mighty ping-pong balls that have enslaved humans for centuries.
b. Hee hee! Silly ping-pong ball swirls in toilet!
c. The police will soon be here because you are playing mean tricks on innocent ping-pong balls.

Check your answer below.[1]

_____

1. If you chose "A," beware! Ping-pong balls are near. Put this book down and run! If you answered "C," please put this book down, get a grip, and then continue reading. But if you answered "B," congratulations! Put this book down and high-five yourself, and then read on.

33

By the way, there is a fourth type of mischief, which is the kind that a person makes without even realizing it. For example, think about that kid in class who mindlessly "clicks" his pen in and out, in and out. Click. Click. Click. Click. Annoying. Make sure that if you click your pen repeatedly, you're at least doing it on purpose. You've got to mean it!

BY THE TIME YOU FINISH THIS BOOK, PEOPLE WILL BE EXPECTING A LOT FROM YOU, SO THINK OF YOURSELF AS AN ARTIST.

Be creative with the approach that you take to life! For instance, let me think of a dull activity a misguided imp might think was a prank. I've got it: finger drumming!

Sure, finger drumming might bother your Nemesis, but studies show that any person with fingers (or really flexible toes) can do it. To take finger drumming to a whole new level, borrow four thimbles from, uh, someone who collects thimbles. Put the thimbles on four of your fingertips (on the same hand, smarty) and start finger drumming. This is guaranteed to get people's attention!

Of course, that was a primitive example. But if you work hard on your prankster skills, you will be able to graduate to an advanced degree: a Master's of Mischief (M.M.) People will come to appreciate your demented genius, especially during tough times. After all, if worse comes to worst, that means that someone who is bad will be the best of all!

Now let's get started! As an aspiring mischief maker, you should know that the worst noise in the world is the sound of a person vomiting. Yep, there was a survey of over a million people to identify the worst noise ever, and vomiting took top honors. Microphone feedback was the second-worst sound, and a crying baby came in third. (If you are ever babysitting a crying child while your friend is rapping and then he gets microphone feedback and throws up, you would probably win a prize or something.)

But how can you use this information for your own purposes? Be creative! Borrow someone's cell phone and change their ring tone to the sound of someone vomiting. (Sound files of this are available online in case you don't want to record this sound yourself. In fact, you can download one at www.bartking.net right now.) Or leave voicemail or e-mail messages for others with these sounds.

Remember, you're an *artist*, so explore the possibilities.

The Moses Award

Calvin College (Grand Rapids, Michigan) gives its Moses Award to the member of the campus community who plays the most lighthearted and funniest prank of the year. The Moses Award comes with a cash prize of $30, which is paid every year in $1.80 installments.

Or maybe you'd like to consider an easier trick? How about this: try changing the message on your Nemesis's voicemail to "Mr. Baloney." ("Hi, this is Mr. Baloney. I can't take your call right now . . .") Another good idea is to sneak onto your Nemesis's e-mail program when he or she is not around. Look up their "addresses" and find an e-mail list. Then send a harmless and uplifting message using that person's e-mail account:

I LOVE YOU ALL! HAVE A GREAT DAY, MR. BALONEY

If you're tired of electronic tricks, try this. Take a handful of the paper that is used in your printer at home, school, or office. Print the line "[*Insert your name here*] is a genius!" on the bottom of thirty pages. Then take all the papers and put them back into the printer backward. As the pages get printed and sent around, your important message will find a wide audience.

Self~Defense:
How to Avoid Getting Tricked Yourself!

Remember that if something sounds too weird or too good to be true, it probably isn't. As every prankster knows, things are not what they seem! This is especially true of things you read on the Internet or that get sent by e-mail. When you're online, every day is April Fools' Day.[2]

But if someone manages to slip a trick through your defenses, be a good sport about it.

---

2. A good place to find out whether something online is real is www.snopes.com.

1. *ENJOY THE CLEVERNESS OF YOUR OPPONENT AND CONGRATULATE HIM OR HER.*

2. *THEN GET REVENGE.*

Wedgies and Melvins

A *wedgie* occurs when a person approaches someone from behind, grabs the waistband of his underwear, and then pulls the waistband up. An *atomic wedgie* is when the waistband is pulled over a victim's head. (Note: This is illegal in some countries.) While terms vary, if the same thing happens from the victim's front, it is called a *melvin*.

Your Nemesis will try to sneak up quietly behind you. He will bend his knees slightly and position his feet under his shoulders. Then in one ultrafast move, he will grab your underwear band and lift while straightening out his legs. If he does it right, you will go off-balance and will be at his mercy while he continues trying for an atomic wedgie. The screams will be incredible!

Safety Tip! If you ever make the mistake of giving someone a wedgie, you have to beware of your vengeance-seeking victim giving one back to you. That means you can never let anyone else walk behind you for the rest of your life. Unfortunately, we can't endorse the "No Underwear = No Wedgie" strategy that some people use. (That's pretty horrible!) Instead, try using this amazing product:

Wedgie-Proof Underwear

40

The Money Game

Like wedgies, the best thing to know about the Money Game is that you should avoid it. It's a simple con game that suckers people all the time. Here's how it works: Let's say a guy named Chad comes up and asks, "Want to play a friendly game?"

You agree. (After all, you're friendly!) Chad puts down a dollar bill. "Now you put a dollar down too," he says. So you do. There are now two dollars on the table. This is the Pot.

"Now we bid on the Pot," Chad says. "The person with the highest bid pays the other person the bid and gets to keep the Pot. It's that simple! I'll start. I bid fifty cents to win all that money."

You think, *If he wins the Pot with that bid, I'm out a dollar!*

You say, "Oh yeah? Well I bid a dollar!"

41

"I bid $1.25," Chad says.

"I bid $1.50," you say. You're still thinking that you'll make a profit of $.50.

Chad says, "Okay, I guess you win the Pot."

You take the two dollars in the Pot and pay Chad $1.50 for it. But now you are out a total of **$2.50**. Since the pot was only **$2**, you lost **fifty cents** to Chad! It's funny, but people never seem to realize this. But at least now you won't be one of the suckers!

Bum Photo

Learn how to use the delay timer on your family's camera. Then at the next party or family get-together, be the person who is in charge of a group photo. Get everyone in the shot, set the timer, and start walking to the group to get in the picture.

Right in front of the camera, act like you see a coin on the floor and bend over to pick it up. This will put your bum in front of the camera when it takes the photo, capturing everyone else freaking out ("It's going to go off!") and your bum (which doesn't have a lot to say).

Piercing Snores

You've seen people with tongue and lip piercings before. Did you know that these cause drooling and chipped teeth? Sweet! If you have a Nemesis who's a heavy sleeper, load him into a van while he's hibernating. Take him to an unethical, all-night piercing parlor and let the piercers pierce away! (While you're there, have them ink a tattoo reading "*[Insert your name here] rules!*" on his arm.)

When your victim wakes up, it will give you a chance to really mean it when you say, "You've got holes in your head!"

Who Said That?

Your parents may
have a baby monitor
still in the house from
when they wanted to
monitor your activities
closely. (You know, like
yesterday?) If you have
access to it, use the monitor
for your own purposes. Want
to know what your sister
talks about on the phone?
Stash the monitor in her room
and stay tuned. Be careful not
to leave the wrong component in
her room; if you do, she could hear *you*
trying to listen to her.

Along similar lines, you may have
walkie-talkies in the house. These are
good for all kinds of nonsense, especially
if you have a pet. See if you can attach
a walkie-talkie to your dog's collar or
near a spot that your cat likes to nap.
Remove yourself from the area with the

other walkie-talkie and wait. As soon as a visitor or family member gets close to the pet, be ready!

IN YOUR BEST ANIMAL VOICE, TRY SAYING SOMETHING LIKE:

"DO YOU THINK I'M CUTE?"

"GEE, YOUR HAIR SMELLS TERRIFIC."

"IF YOU HAVE A MINUTE, MY LEFT EAR IS ITCHY."

"YOU KNOW WHAT SOUNDS GOOD RIGHT NOW? NACHOS!"

Who Wants Gum? Pouaghh!

When you're chewing gum, have you ever noticed how if you drink something, the gum stiffens up, loses its flavor, and is ruined?

What happens is that gum gets soft at a

fairly high temperature. Since the inside of your mouth is almost 100 degrees F, that's hot enough to do the trick. But if a beverage hits the gum, it stiffens up even harder than it was before you put it in your mouth. If you have some friends coming over, put some sticks of gum in the refrigerator. Once they arrive, reinsert the cold sticks into the pack at the bottom. Then offer gum to everyone!

Or give them warm gum first and try to get them to drink something ice cold. As your victims weep and despair at the stiff rubber in their mouths, be sure not to tell them that drinking something warm will soften the gum up again.

H_2O My Gosh, That's Funny

I love to open bottled water, sip it, and then loudly exclaim, "This bottled water has gone sour!" Hikers know that one of the heaviest things to pack around is water. On your next hiking trip, claim to have found a way around this problem. Tell everyone that you have brought a container of powdered water. If anyone asks you how it works, say, "You just add water."

Sometimes it can be disastrous to add *yourself* to water. I'm talking about belly flops here! If you have ever flopped, you know how painful it can be to hit the water wrong. But how can water hurt us? Isn't it the "softest" thing around?

To understand why flopping sucks, you need to know that the water in a pool or lake has this thing called "surface tension." Basically, the water molecules at the top of the water's surface bond more powerfully with the air above and the water molecules below than they would otherwise. And that's why a belly flop can hurt so much!

Surface tension also explains why you can skip stones on water. The record for skipping a stone is held by Jerdone Coleman-McGhee. He skipped a rock thirty-eight times! Jerdone used a flat rock with small holes in the surface. He then threw the rock at exactly twenty-five miles per hour and at a 20-degree angle to the water. (Bring a radar gun and protractor to the water's edge to achieve Jerdone's level of success.)

Find a projectile device that can fire *you* at twenty-five mph and at a 20-degree angle across a lake. See how many times you skip across.

While we're getting watery, try to time your toilet visits so that you have a pressing need when someone is in the shower. Nothing is as satisfying as "taking care of business," flushing, and then hearing the surprised hoots of someone whose shower has just gotten very cold . . . or hot!

If you're looking for more ambitious watery humor, grease up a watermelon and throw it into a swimming pool. You won't be able to stop laughing as people try to get their hands on it (until they get their hands on you and throw you into the pool after your melon).

Can't afford a watermelon? Here's a moneymaking idea. If you or a younger brother or sister lose a tooth, put it under the pillow as usual, but also rig a snare around it. This will allow you to catch the Tooth Fairy, who, from what I hear, carries a large amount of cash on her.

Personal Silliness!

Single adults place personal ads for themselves in newspapers and online to meet people and make romantic connections. In the United States, single adults think the idea is to make themselves sound good, and so they use words like *attractive*, *successful*, *intelligent*, *sweet*, and so on. (In other words, they lie.) This results in nauseating ads like "Extremely fit, beautiful, and highly successful 30-year-old woman with sizzling eyes

(continued on next page)

seeks Justin Timberlake look-alike for dancing and romantic dinners."

You may begin throwing up now.

But in England, it's a different story. Talk about mischief makers! When the writers of the personal ads in the *London Review of Books* describe themselves, they use words like *plaid-wearing*, *shallow*, *gassy*, and *bald*. Here are some personal favorites:

"Flatulent British gnome, toothless, does not seek romantic sunsets."

"Writing this ad has given me the greatest sense of accomplishment since successfully ironing my pants for the first time (on June 14, 1998)."

"This ad may not be the best personal in the world, nor its author the best smelling. That's all I have to say. Man, 37."

"I am not an accountant."

"Ppfffftttt, ssshhhhhhhhwwwwt, peeffwt, pffpt. Man, 36. Bad at whistling."

Oldies but Goodies

Old people are cool! Old people are especially cool because they are happy to see you doing anything that doesn't include newfangled inventions like the computer, the abacus, or video games. There's nothing a person of advanced age likes as much as a high-spirited young person engaged in tomfoolery. Oh, and skullduggery. Older folks love skullduggery! And they love younger folks like you who have

51

a little pep in their step and who will talk to them.

YOU: *WOW, GRANDMA, YOU'RE OLD-SCHOOL.*

GRANDMA: *NOT QUITE. I'M FROM THE SCHOOL THEY TORE DOWN TO BUILD THE OLD SCHOOL!*

(YOU BOTH LAUGH HEARTILY.)

Be careful when greeting your grand-parents. Sure, you want to squeeze the stuffing out of Grandpa, but can you hear those cracks? Those are his ribs breaking. As for Grandma, be careful when you do air kisses with her. You may accidentally give her the air kiss of death, which will not be amusing for anyone.

On the down side, for some reason older people just love to talk about how their joints ache or their pancreas is wheezing. This can be annoying, especially since they are usually faking it to get atten-tion. One way to deal with this is to listen very attentively as your older friend or

relative tells you the fascinating details
of how his feet smell and his nose runs.
(You might even want to take notes.)

THEN NOD WISELY AND SAY:

★ *"I DIAGNOSE THIS PROBLEM AS NOSTALGIA. TAKE
TWO FLINTSTONES VITAMINS AND CALL ME IN
THE MORNING."*

★ *"BASED ON THIS INFORMATION, I KNOW WHAT
THE PROBLEM IS. YOU'VE HAD TOO MANY
BIRTHDAYS."*

★ *"I'M AFRAID YOUR UNIVERSAL JOINT IS ABOUT
TO GIVE WAY. DO YOU HAVE ANY WD-40?"*

Your elderly patient will either chuckle or
start to chase you while swinging a cane
or hickory stick. (If so, remind them that
you are not a licensed doctor and respectfully run away.)

If you'd like another fun activity to do with
your grandfather, ask him to make you a
telephone of two tin cans and a piece of

Old~School Pranks

★ Super glue a quarter or dollar coin to the ground.
★ Spread plastic wrap under the toilet seat.
★ When someone is sitting, tie their shoelaces together.
★ Put ketchup, Desitin, or Brylcreem in the toothpaste tube.
★ Make ice cubes with rubber bugs in them.

string. Act like this is the greatest thing that you've ever seen, and then ask how to download ring tones to it.

There are other fun diversions you can take part in with older folks. And the beauty of it is that they are so much simpler to deal with than other age groups! For example, they love playing old-fashioned games like "Hide and Go to Sleep" and "Simon Says *What*?!"

Staring contests are passé, so consider having a bladder contest instead. Contestants young and old should chug a quart of fluid and then stare at a lawn sprinkler or Doughboy pool. (This will be especially good for your self esteem, because Gramps isn't going to last five minutes.)

SINCE OLDER FOLKS LOVE OUTINGS, LET ME SUGGEST THAT YOU VISIT TATTOO JOINTS AND PIERCING PARLORS.

World Wide Web Warning!

The Internet has not been cleaned for years, and is full of dead links and empty domain names. To improve performance, the Internet will be shut down for one week, starting tomorrow. Please keep your computer turned off during that time so that the hard drive is not accidentally erased.

There's nothing quite as impressive as open-heart surgery scars with flame tattoos, or dentures with a pierced tongue.

WARNING: PIERCED TONGUES MAY IMPAIR OCTOGENARIANS FROM CLEARLY ENUNCIATING "BINGO!"

In the course of these activities, you will form a close relationship with some lucky older person. Let me encourage you to confide your deepest, darkest secrets to your new old companion. After all, who is he going to tell? He won't be able to remember them!

Thank you for supporting the older generation. After all, they are the key to the future! (Of course, I'm defining the future as just the next couple of years.)

Practical Jokes

INSPIRED BY ANCIENT ROME

"HE WHO HAS A MIND TO DO MISCHIEF WILL ALWAYS FIND A PRETENSE." —*Publilius Syrus*

Pranks and hoaxes have a great historical tradition. For example, back in the days of the ancient Romans, the Saturnalia festival was a time for dancing, mischief, and playing jokes. Masters let their slaves boss them around, and a fake king named the Lord of Misrule ruled for a day making mischief.

If the Lord of Misrule were here today,

Mischief	Evil
★ LETTING THE AIR OUT OF YOUR NEMESIS'S TRICYCLE TIRES.	★ REMOVING THE AIR FROM THE ENTIRE PLANET.
★ DRESSING UP IN A GORILLA COSTUME AND WALKING DOWN YOUR STREET WHILE EATING A BANANA.	★ RELEASING A WILD GORILLA INTO YOUR NEIGHBORHOOD.
★ PASSING GAS AND THEN BLAMING YOUR NEMESIS.	★ PASSING GAS AND THEN TAKING CREDIT FOR IT YOURSELF.

I'm sure he would remind us to never let a practical joke be mean-spirited or stupid. What's the point of that? A good practical joke can be one of the greatest things in the world. It inspires laughter and good spirits. But a bad one can be a total disaster, and if it's a mean one, it is actually *evil*. So before learning about the following practical jokes, let's look at the table on page 58 and compare the difference between mischief and plain old evil. (Oh, and by the way, evil-doers can never work for Google.[1])

Now, on to some simple pranks!

First, let's spice up some leftovers.

Almost everyone already knows the trick about wrapping a rubber band around the handle on the hose in the kitchen sink or outdoors. (You know,

---

1. Google's corporate motto is "Don't be evil."

when a victim turns on the water, he or she gets sprayed.) Since people know to beware of these rubber bands, try using fishing line instead! No one will be able to spot it, and the prank will be twice as funny when it works on someone who knows better.

Another prank that barely qualifies as a joke is leaving rubber bugs or spiders lying around. Ho hum. But if you put these same bugs under washrags or pillows, the extra element of surprise can throw a fright into someone. Also, if you can master needle and thread, stitch a rubber bug onto the shoulder of someone's old sweater, sweatshirt, or coat. Then when your Nemesis puts on the garment, the bug will be so close to his or her face that there is no choice but to freak out!

ONCE I PLAYED A JOKE ON MYSELF JUST BY BEING STUPID.

In my calendar book I had written down "3:15! Very Important" on a particular date. The problem was that as I got closer to that day, I had no idea why I had written that there. I waited with dread and anticipation for that day and its Very Important time to roll around. Was it an appointment? Would a fire start if I wasn't at the right place? And what would happen if I didn't show up?

It turned out that 3:15 came and went, and as far as I know, nobody died because I wasn't in the right spot. In honor of my most foolhardy knuckleheadedness,

I NOW WRITE "3:15! VERY IMPORTANT" ON RANDOM DATES ON OTHER PEOPLE'S CALENDARS AND IN THEIR BLACKBERRIES AND APPOINTMENT BOOKS.

Just Chillin'

Putting an ice cube down someone's shirt isn't very original. But nobody can deny that the trick gets better if you say, "Freeze a jolly good fellow!" while you do it.

I Love You Just the Age You Are

Your parents will love this. Write a note that reads, "Objects in the mirror are older than they appear." Then tape it to the mirror in your parents' bathroom. Try to arrange it so that they don't notice the note until they wake up in the morning.

Though I hate to admit it, here's a prank that was successfully played on me. For a time, my Nemesis was a man named Andy Lennox. As payback for a charming and innocent joke I had played on him, Andy placed a free classified ad in the newspaper listing my VW van for sale for $50. What a vicious man! I learned that newspapers hit newsstands at 5 a.m., because that's when I got my first of many phone calls for the van. When I figured out what happened, I left a message on my voice mail telling callers that the car was already sold. And I still got fifty-two messages!

Score one for the Nemesis. I share this story with you so that you can learn from my mistake: never have a Nemesis named Andy.

Even with revenge on my mind, I still didn't consider toilet papering Andy's house. After all, TPing is wasteful! Think of all the bottom wiping that paper could have been used for! More importantly, TPing is what is legally known as "criminal mischief," or damaging property that you don't own. Admittedly, the damage that toilet paper can inflict is minimal, but don't say I didn't warn you.

A Taste of Your Own Medicine

Are guests coming over? Comedian Amy Sedaris came up with the idea of stacking marbles in the medicine cabinet before guests arrive. That way you'll know if they are the nosy types. If they go snooping, your marble alarm system will go off!

But just in case you get swept up in a mob and carried against your will to a TPing event, remember, there is a way to throw a roll of toilet paper from so far away, you won't have to worry about getting caught. How is this possible? I have two words for you: leaf blower. Just stick the roll on the end of the blower and then blow. Toilet paper goes bye-bye. (And it unrolls all the way!)

A POPULAR NIGHTTIME PRANK IS "FORKING" SOMEONE'S LAWN WITH DOZENS, HUNDREDS, OR THOUSANDS OF PLASTIC PICNIC FORKS AND SPELLING OUT SOMETHING LIKE "CLASS OF 2010" WITH THEM.

Geography 101

The students of Southern California's Caltech transformed the fifty-foot-high letters above Los Angeles reading "Hollywood" to "Caltech." Tourists to the area were completely baffled. "We're on a college campus?"

Deadly Inflation

Little kids love to pop balloons, so why not encourage them in this wholesome activity? Get some balloons and sprinkle a little flour in them. Then take some small strips of paper and write special messages on them. I recommend statements like "Why did you kill me?" and "My life was so short." Put the strips in the balloons, and then blow the balloons up and hand them out.

Forking is a lot of work; I recommend using instant potato flakes instead. They are easier to pour out, biodegradable, and the dew will make the flakes get puffy and round by morning. (Note: the potato flake trick doesn't work so well in the desert.)

One of the most wholesome mischief makers around is a man named Paul Curtis. He invented something called "clean tagging." What Paul does is find a portion of public property, like a dirty sidewalk or grimy building wall, and then he cleans it with scrubbing and elbow grease. And as Paul cleans, he creates a picture or writes words that are revealed by the clean parts. Hey, he's a grime writer! (If you want to copy his example, don't worry. This is not vandalism, and you don't need a permit to clean city property.)

IF YOU HAVE A NEMESIS (OR ANYONE ELSE!) IN YOUR HOUSEHOLD WHO USES WHITE "STICK" DEODORANT, CONSIDER THIS TRICK.

White House Monkeyshines

It turns out that when a politician moves out of his or her office to make room for the newly elected replacement, it's a good time for silly pranks. For example, when George W. Bush first came to the White House in 2000, his workers found that Bill Clinton's staff had glued desk drawers shut, left weird voice mail messages, and even stolen the "W" key off many computer keyboards.

PRACTICAL JOKES

Seeing Double

If you know any twins, bring them with you into a Kinko's or other photocopy store. Take them to the counter and say, "This isn't what I ordered!" Extra credit for bringing in triplets, quadruplets, or septuplets.

To play it, you'll need some cream cheese. First, roll the deodorant out maybe a half inch. Make a note of its general shape, and then cut off the end of it with a butter knife.

Now roll the stick back in so that you can see a half-inch gap inside the container. Take a butter knife and fill in that space with cream cheese. Now once again roll the stick out a little bit and try to shape the cream cheese so that it resembles what the stick looked like in the first place. Put the deodorant's cap back on and be patient!

67

Professional football player Steve McKinney shared this prank that he played on rookies in training camp. (You are not allowed to try it without good planning and the help of a responsible adult.) Steve would get his hands on a player's car keys. Then he would take a clear glass bottle, wrap it in several paper bags, and break the bottle by gently hitting the outside of the bags with a hammer. He would then take the keys, the bag of broken glass, some gloves and a brick, and go to the rookie's car.

Once there, he would unlock the car and roll down the driver's window. He would put on the gloves and pick up some of the biggest (and easiest to clean up later) glass pieces. He would set these on the driver's seat and then place the brick on top of them. Closing the door, he would flee the scene of the crime and try to watch later when the rookie would go out to his car and think that it was broken into!

Free Speech, $1

Protestors are almost always mischief makers, but sometimes that's what it takes to make a difference in this world. Some protestors are having fun, some are serious, and some are dolts. See if you can tell which kind of protestors the following stories describe!

1. On December 31, 2006, French demonstrators in the city of Nantes marched against the New Year by carrying banners that read "Now is better!" and "No to 2007!" They wanted to stop the "mad race" of time and suspend the future. And when 2007 came anyway, the protestors started chanting, "No to 2008!"

2. Snowboarders in Romania protested about the lack of snow due

(continued on next page)

69

to global warming. The snowboarders held their protest in front of Romania's national weather institute, in the hopes that this might affect the weather. The protestors left only after weathermen told them their complaint "would be passed on to a higher authority."

3. To protest the world's dependence on oil, thousands of bicyclists saddle up each year for the World Naked Bike Ride. This protest began in Canada in 2004 and seems to be getting larger each year. Protestors put on bike helmets (and nothing else!) and pedal in groups to show their support for the cause.

Another great trick I'll share with you is called One Ring. While it sounds like something from *Lord of the Rings*, it's actually an easy and harmless trick to play with a group of people on a single Nemesis. For this example, we will pretend that the Nemesis is a sports fan. Let's say he loves the Portland Trail Blazers. Any time something goes wrong with the team—they lose in overtime, their best player is traded, their arena sinks into the ground and disappears—you call your Nemesis. You let the phone ring once, and then hang up. And now this part is key: have everyone you know also call your Nemesis, let it ring once, and then hang up.

That's the beauty of One Ring. If you do it every time something bad happens, your Nemesis will come to dread it. And if his or her cell phone isn't set properly, it's possible that your One Ring could catch your Nemesis in class. That's extra credit for you: a One Ring and a bawling out by the teacher! If you're lucky enough to see this happen in person, wait until the punishment ends, and then One Ring

Budding Picasso

Know anyone who wears glasses? Have any tempera or watercolor paints? Why not paint over those glasses? Not only will it provide a chuckle, the paint will wash right off.

The Greatest Crimes Never Committed

Brian Hughes was a successful businessman who loved a creative prank. Among other things, he was known for leaving imitation jewelry outside of expensive stores like Tiffany's. Hughes then enjoyed watching people steal the "treasure" and run off. Hughes also once put empty picture frames and burglar tools in front of the Metropolitan Museum of Art, leading panicked employees to think that the museum's paintings had just been stolen.

him again. It's a good way to trash talk without talking!

Oh, and don't be surprised if your phone starts ringing one ring at a time once One Ring starts to gain popularity.

Amusing Slights AND FRIENDLY JIBES

> *"MISCHIEF IS MERELY AN ATTEMPT TO ESCAPE FROM THE DREARY VACUUM OF IDLENESS."* —*George Borrow*

Now that you have gotten this far into the book, you have probably found yourself becoming more popular with other people. It can't be helped! Babies are jumping out of their strollers and chasing after you. ("Oh my gosh, little Timmy can walk!") Kids are following you around, attracted by your magnetic personality. And adults are now looking at you with a mixture of interest and concern.

As you receive invitation after invitation to birthday parties, bat mitzvahs, concerts, and hamster fights, you're going to need some good excuses. Feel free to use these:

★ SORRY, MY MOMMY WON'T LET ME.

★ I'LL BE AT A SOLITAIRE CONVENTION ON THAT DATE.

★ YOUR CATS ARE ALLERGIC TO ME.

★ DARN, I WILL BE ON A HAYRIDE THEN!

★ I HAVE (PICK ONE): LICE, TICKS, RINGWORM, LEPROSY, A SWOLLEN XIPHOID.

★ I HAVE TO DYE MY HAIR THAT DAY.

★ MY (DOG, CAT, MOOSE) DIED AND I HAVE TO BURY IT.

★ I'LL HAVE TO CHECK WITH MY SECRETARY TO SEE IF MY CALENDAR IS OPEN THEN.

If you have some strange desire to have even more friends, here are a couple of tips. First, learn to fake interest in what other people have to say. (This is very effective.) Better yet, learn hypnosis. Then you'll make very dedicated friends. In fact, you might even get a Sidekick who is worthy of you.

AND THERE IS A VERY GOOD REASON TO HAVE A SIDEKICK. HE OR SHE CAN HELP YOU DEAL WITH ALL THE OTHER WANNABES AND HANGERS-ON BY STARTING A FAN CLUB.

For you! Yes, some folks might think it odd if you set up your own fan club, but a trustworthy Sidekick can easily do it. Let him or her set up the club, as long as he or she follows this rule: a person has to pay a small fee to join your club. And you're the Club Treasurer.

Speaking of sidekicks, back in Jolly Olde England, a young man looking to be a royal Sidekick could get the job of Whipping Boy. The rule was that a royal prince could not be punished for any trouble that he got into. Instead, his Whipping Boy (a kid about the prince's age) was whipped and spanked for the prince's crimes. What a job! The theory was that the prince would feel so guilty about subjecting his innocent Sidekick to punishment, he would be good. (Like that's going to work.)

Maybe you can persuade your Sidekick to fill a similar role for you. He could be your Detention Boy. After all, there comes a time in every mischief maker's life when he or she gets in trouble. Perhaps you took a practical joke too far or said the wrong thing at the wrong time to the wrong person?

ASSUMING THAT YOU ARE IN THE WRONG (COULD IT BE?), THE FIRST THING TO DO IS APOLOGIZE.

Of course, the problem is that everyone will think that you're only sorry because you got in trouble. Like my mom said to me last week, "You aren't sorry or you wouldn't have done it in the first place." But luckily for you, if you really are sorry for what you did, others will see that you are sincere and they will forgive you. (I think.)

IF YOU GET CAUGHT UP IN THE SPIRIT OF YOUR APOLOGY AND START TO CRY TEARS OF REGRET, THAT'S OKAY.

Mischief makers cry all the time! (In fact, I'm crying as I write this.) But if you don't want others to know that your tears are flowing, tell them, "I'm not crying. It's raining on my face."

You don't need my help on how to be sincere.[1] But if you're going to apologize, make sure to do a good job. A bad apology is like a second insult! So avoid the following apology styles. They don't work!

---

1. If you do need help: make good eye contact, say "I apologize for . . . ," and keep it short.

The Blame~Shifting Apology:

I said it, but I didn't say it!

Example: "I was merely repeating a comment made decades ago [by someone else]." —*Earl Butz, 1976*

The Non~Apology Apology:

I apologize for what I did, but not for myself.

Example: "Regrettably, some of the words I've used have hurt some people." —*Dr. Laura Schlesinger, 2000*

The "Huh?" Apology:

What did he say?

Example: "I shouldn't have said something that I said. I'm sorry. I'll never say it again." —*Gary Spears, 1987*

> "Two wrongs don't make a right, but they make
> a good excuse." —Thomas Szasz

The "I Am the Real Victim Here" Apology:

So I made one little mistake!

Example: "I am the victim of an error of judgment." —*Adolph Eichmann, 1961*

The Long Speech Apology:

By the time I finish, you'll forget what I did wrong.

Example: "How things happen, why things happen, we don't always know. But I would like to apologize for what did happen. There were a lot of human factors. There were a lot of victims . . . in a funny way, I've learned a lot."
—*Bruce McNall, 1997*[2]

---

2. He was just getting started.

The "You Don't Understand Me" Apology:

I'm smarter than you.

Example: "I offer my full apology to [anyone] who misinterpreted my remarks."
—*Donald Rumsfeld, 2003*

If you really are *not* sorry, it's some-times best not to apologize unless you really have to. After all, you're a mischief maker, not a liar. Still, some people think it's okay to apologize as long as you just act sincere. For them it's a case of "Once you can fake sincerity, you've got it made." But I disagree. Most people can spot a liar pretty well, and most people don't like liars. No lie. So tell the truth![3]

A particularly good excuse is this one: "I'm sorry, it's just that I'm at a difficult

---

3. Of course, the truth is sometimes a slippery thing. What is the truth? If you're in trouble, maybe you should tell the most hopeful version of the truth.

age." If you can say that with the right expression, you just might get off easy. And the beauty of it is, it doesn't matter what age you are. All ages can be difficult!

Other Excellent All~Purpose Excuses

"Let's let bygones be bygones."

Since no one knows what a "bygone" actually is, this will confuse your opponent, allowing you to slip away unharmed.

"Forgive and forget."

If this line doesn't work, try just shouting "Forgive!" Still nothing? Give "Forget!" a shot. (Good luck.)

"I guess I'm a dreamer."

A personal favorite.

Past Posterior Posterity

In French, the words *faux pas* (foe-pa) mean "false step." When a person makes an embarrassing remark, it is often called a faux pas. Sir Winston Churchill (1874–1965) was a great prime minister of the United Kingdom, and he made one of my favorite faux pas. Churchill was giving a speech in Paris, and he tried to say "When I consider what is behind me" in French. His audience started chuckling, and after his speech, Churchill learned that he had *actually* said, "When I consider my behind, I can state that it is divided into two equal parts."[4]

"I'm just a kid. I don't understand a lot of things yet."

Use this one only if you're desperate and under thirty.

---

4. "Quand je considère mon derrière, je constate qu'il est divisé en deuz parties égales."

More Specific Excuses for Creative Optimists like You!

"I have to do my homework? Okay, but what will I tell the orphans? They'll still be expecting story hour."

"I'd like to clean my room, but my dirty laundry is protecting the floor from scratches."

"I would love to dance with you, but this song was playing when my best friend died in a tragic loofah accident, and it brings back bad memories."

For Younger Readers

If what you have done is particularly bad, an adult may be displeased with you. This is a good time to say, in a sad, innocent voice, "There is no such thing as a bad child. Just bad childhoods."

"I only got a poor grade on the test because the teacher restricts free speech and only accepts so-called 'correct answers.' I intend to study law and put an end to this barbaric practice."

Word Fu

Impress your friends! Devastate your Nemesis! Using Word Fu, you can think of your Nemesis as a tree, and cut him or her down to size. But be sure to use your insults with style. As word expert Michael Wex wrote, a good insult is not "a matter of yelling out bad words; the trick is to put good ones together in the most damaging way." But let's not be too harsh. A friendly jibe or amusing slight should always be used instead of a hard-core humiliating put-down. That way you can have fun and strengthen the relationship you have with your Nemesis.[5] (The two of you will be so happy together.)

_____

5. This process is known as "busting someone's chops" or "giving someone the business."

The first technique of Word Fu is to strike when someone asks you a silly question.

YOUR DAD: **HOW WAS SCHOOL TODAY?**

YOU: **I'M PRETTY SURE THE POLICE WILL BE FILLING YOU IN ON THAT LATER.**

Speaking of police, let's say your dad gets pulled over by a police officer while you're in the car with him. It's almost a sure thing that the officer will ask your dad, "Do you know why I pulled you over?" Since this is a potentially silly question, both your dad and the officer might appreciate your sharp wit if you say, "We were hoping that you knew!"

One silly question I get a lot happens when I'm talking on the phone. A person will come in the room, see me, and ask, "Are you on the phone?" One answer I like

Another important martial art for the mischief maker: *nogethitsu.*

to give is, "No, but shhhh, I love this dial tone."

Here's a question I often get when I'm buying something. The clerk will ask, "Will there be anything else?" Try answering, "Not right now, but I plan on coming back and buying everything here one item at a time." If you are asked what size you are, your answer should be, "Actual size." Or think about the next time you go to the doctor's office. The odds are pretty high that a nurse or the doctor will ask, "So how are you doing today?" To which you can say, "I'm fine, I just like hanging out here."

Writer Al Jaffee used to write *MAD* magazine features devoted to "Snappy Answers to Stupid Questions." One of my favorites is this one:

"ARE YOU ASLEEP?"

"NO, I'M DEAD. LEAVE YOUR FLOWERS AND GET OUT."

Even though you are a good person, it is inevitable that at some time in your life, someone will say this to you:

"YOU !@&$?!"*

TO WHICH YOU SHOULD ANSWER, "YOU CAN CALL ME [INSERT YOUR NAME HERE]."

But it is possible to get carried away with "clever" responses. For example, a nice cook who was making a meal for me asked if I was allergic to anything.

ME: I'M ALLERGIC TO POISON MUSHROOMS, POISON FISH, POISON VEGETABLES—

PERSON: SO BASICALLY, YOU'RE ALLERGIC TO POISON?

ME: RIGHT!

The cook was so annoyed by my comments, my meal was poisoned. (But I got better.) Anyway, no book can provide you with all the comeback lines you'll need for the

Ye Olde Oldy - Moldy
COMEBACK LIST

These are the oldest comebacks in the world. Know them so that you know NEVER to use them, even in an emergency.

1. OH YEAH?

2. YOU AND WHOSE ARMY?

3. NOT. AS IF. PSYCH!

4. AT LEAST MY MOM DOESN'T WEAR ARMY BOOTS.

5. SAYS YOU.

6. I REFUSE TO HAVE A BATTLE OF WITS WITH AN UNARMED OPPONENT.

7. AND THEN YOU WOKE UP.

8. I'M RUBBER AND YOU'RE GLUE. WHATEVER YOU SAY BOUNCES OFF ME AND STICKS TO YOU.

9. I HOPE YOU USE YOUR GENIUS FOR GOOD AND NOT EVIL.

10. YOU HAVE BAD BREATH AND YOUR MOTHER DRESSES YOU FUNNY.

rest of your life. So keep your wits keen and come up with your own ideas!

The Sucker Punch

The next technique in Word Fu is creating an insult that is a combination of something nice (or neutral) with something nasty. The key is to begin your comment with the "nice" part. That way, your Nemesis will let his guard down, thinking, "Oh, this appears to be a compliment." Then, wham! Sucker punch! This is a little like the backhanded compliment, where you start off by saying something nice, but then there's a little twist at the end.

This technique probably comes from the old-fashioned Yiddish curse. In Jewish culture, an insult is often a curse. You tell your Nemesis that you hope he will get what he wants from life and yet still be miserable: "May you always be healthy and strong, and always be asking what the weather outside is like." Your Nemesis has to think about what you're saying, and that's where the curse gets its power.

Sucker Punch examples:

★ *"YOU REALLY MAKE ME FEEL INTELLIGENT, ESPECIALLY WHEN YOU TALK."*

★ *"WHAT I LIKE ABOUT YOUR CLOTHES IS THAT THEY SAY, 'HEY, I HAVE BETTER THINGS TO SPEND MY MONEY ON.'"*

★ *"YOU HAVE EIGHT HAMSTERS IN HERE? THAT'S A SURPRISE. IT ONLY SMELLS LIKE THREE OR FOUR."*

★ *"THANK GOODNESS! AT FIRST I THOUGHT YOU BOMBED, BUT IT WAS ONLY YOUR BREATH."*

★ *"HAKUNA MATATA, CHOWDERHEAD."*

"Are you iodine deficient?" is a common insult in Kazakhstan. That's because kids who eat iodized salt have higher IQs than those who don't, and youngsters there often don't get enough iodine in their diets.

The Face/Head/Brain Formula

I'm almost a scientist, and I have found that combining everyday objects with the words "face," "head," or "brain" will often result in a good insult. Of course, most people already know that "butt"[6] works with all of these.

But keep in mind that many foods also work especially well with this pattern. For example, Mutton Head, Taco Face, and Sauerkraut Brain are all perfectly good insults. (Apple and Chowder are also good foods to use.)

---

6. Butt Head, Butt Face, Butt Brain.

Great Moments in Insults I:

"Please try not to be such a wiener-head." —*Dave Barry*

Root vegetables make for excellent insult recipes using this formula. That's why Onion Head, Parsnip Face, and Potato Brain are all guaranteed to bring a smile to the face of even the sourest Radish Head. Heck, you can also get the neck into the action, as in "Hey, Turkey Neck, how about moving your big Onion Head out of the way?" (Hmmm, must be lunchtime.) And some animals (especially primates!) also fit in well with the Face/Head/Brain Formula. You can be general or specific; it's all up to your personal style.

GENERAL	*SPECIFIC*
Ape Face	*Orangutan Face*
Lemur Head	*Ring-tailed Lemur Head*
Monkey Brain	*Crab-eating Macaque Brain*

The Butt/Booty Trick

Maybe it's just me, but if someone is full of baloney, it never seems that satisfying to say, "You're full of baloney." That's why we have the Butt/Booty Trick. If you think someone is not telling the truth, combine a food item with the word "booty" or "butt" to let your Nemesis know that you see through his or her little charade.

Example:

YOUR BROTHER: SERIOUSLY, MOM SAID YOU SHOULD CLEAN UP MY ROOM.

YOU: YOU'RE FULL OF BUTT CHEDDAR!

Great Moments in Insults II:

"They don't hardly make 'em like him any more—but just to be on the safe side, he should be castrated anyway." —*Hunter S. Thompson*

Be prepared!

A Nemesis can come in any type, shape, or size.

TO A NEMESIS WHO IS A "JUNIOR":
"Sequels are never as good as the original."

FOR A GOTH NEMESIS:
"Who let you out of the bat cave?"

TO A NEMESIS WITH A LARGE BUTT:
"You're a proctologist's delight."[7]

TO A NEMESIS EXPERIENCING TECHNICAL DIFFICULTIES:
"You've got more problems than a math textbook."

---

7. A proctologist is a butt doctor.

FOR A NEMESIS WHO JUST DID SOMETHING KLUTZY:
"Smooth move, Ex-Lax."

TO A NEMESIS WHO IS ZONING OUT:
"Your display is on screen-saver."

FOR A NEMESIS WHO FOOLISHLY ASKS FOR YOUR HELP WITH SOMETHING:
"I'd like to help out, but right now I'm busier than a one-legged man at a butt-kicking contest."

TO A SPOILED NEMESIS:
"Ooh, I have to tell the science teacher that I've discovered 'yuppie larva.'"

FOR A SHORT NEMESIS:
"Be careful, or I'll stick you in the microwave and set it to 'High.'"

TO A NEMESIS WITH A SOUR PERSONALITY:
"You've totally passed your 'Eat-by' date."

FOR A NEMESIS WHO IS ACTING LIKE A BIG SHOT:
"Somebody get a cage, because a party animal is on the loose in here!"

FOR A NEMESIS PLAYING MUSIC YOU DON'T LIKE:
"That sounds like a washing machine full of barf."

TO A NEMESIS WHO IS LAZY:
"You are a WOMBAT: A Waste Of Money, Brains, And Time."

FOR A NEMESIS WHO JUST SAID SOMETHING DUMB:
"Your hard drive is full."

TO TWO NEMESES:
Give a thumb's up and say enthusiastically, "You're number 1 and you're number 1. Together, you make number 2!"

FOR A NEMESIS WHO JUST DROPPED BY YOUR HOUSE:

"If I'd known you were coming, I'd have baked a fruitcake."

TO A NEMESIS WHO ASKS YOU HOW THEY WOULD LOOK IN A CERTAIN ARTICLE OF CLOTHING:

"Lonely."

TO A NEMESIS WHO IS PLAYING CHESS, BACKGAMMON, OR ALMOST ANY OTHER BOARD GAME:

"Hey, do you know which piece is the battleship?"

FOR A BRITISH NEMESIS:

"You, sir, are a milk-faced popinjay!"

Manners

You might think that a mischief maker should do just the opposite of what traditional manners say to do. But while writing "thanks-for-nothing" cards, eating soup with a fork, and not showing up for your own parties is a good start, there's a lot more to it than that.

It's not enough to just do the *opposite* of what is polite. You want to be thought of as a genius, not some predictable creep. So make a point of acting polite almost all the time. This will lull people into thinking that you actually *are* polite. Ha ha!

That means that when you are in a social situation, people will expect your normal, polite behavior. And that's when it's time to strike! If you're at a party or visiting a relative, tell your hostess, "This was the best party I've ever been to!" If she asks you how many parties you've been to, say, "None," and then burst out crying. (No, really, if you can make yourself cry, do it.

Otherwise, just fake it. I fake cry all the time. It usually gets the neighborhood kids to stop shooting arrows at me.)

Or let's say that you get to introduce two people to each other. Most people would make introductions by saying the person's name and something interesting about them. To this formula, you can add your own little twist:

"JIM, PLEASE MEET MY FRIEND NAKEELA. JIM WAS IN PRISON FOR FIVE YEARS. NAKEELA LIKES TO JUGGLE MARMOTS."

If you're at someone's house for dinner and they ask you where you'd like to sit, quote famous mischief maker H. L. Mencken: "Wherever I sit is the head of the table." Oh, and when you leave, be

According to a *Reader's Digest* poll, the most polite cities in North America are New York, Toronto, and Mexico City. Avoid these places at all costs.

sure to say something like, "I've had a great time. Only this wasn't it."

And remember that you can also spruce up even the rudest of activities with a little class of your own. For example, Wet Willies (sticking your finger in your mouth and then sticking it in someone's ear) are disgusting and should be avoided.

But if you have no choice and absolutely have to do one, use the more polite version of this prank. It is known as the Watery William. For this, you wet your finger with mineral water and say "Excuse me" as you stick your finger in the other person's ear. When you pull the finger out, you say, "I deeply regret that."

Then you politely run away.

Spy Games

"THERE IS NOTHING MORE NECES-SARY THAN GOOD INTELLIGENCE TO FRUSTRATE A DESIGNING ENEMY."
—*George Washington*

It's important for you to develop spying skills to use on prime target #1: your Nemesis. While gathering intelligence on someone as unintelligent as your Nemesis seems silly, remember that it's important to know your enemy. The first step for you to work on to accomplish this goal is *skulking*. This is the art of moving about so stealthily, you're invisible to the world's innocent, unsuspecting people. (The fools!)

SKULKING TIP #1: MOVE ALONG WALLS AND STAY OUT OF THE OPEN.

SKULKING TIP #2: LOOK AS IF YOU'RE CONCEALING SOMETHING.

SKULKING TIP #3: IF YOU STOP MOVING, YOU MUST LURK. THIS IS BEST DONE IN DARKENED CORNERS AND DOORWAYS.

Once you've mastered skulking and lurking, you need to invest in some espionage equipment. For starters, I have one word for you: *periscope*. With a periscope, you can peer over walls, around corners, and out of lockers. This lets you know if danger is coming (Girl Scouts!) without giving away your position. Other important equipment to have with you at all times includes a briefcase (much cooler than a Hello Kitty backpack), a paper shredder (for destroying documents), a lie detector (don't use it on yourself), and a jar of peanut butter (for nutrition! And pack a spoon as well).

When I'm staking out my Nemesis, I sometimes bring along my one-eyed sidekick, Hans Knickerbocker. (He lost an eye in an unfortunate rubber-band incident.) While it's helpful to have one more eye on the street, Hans refuses to

Agent 003

James Bond was invented by British writer Ian Fleming in 1953. Fleming himself had experience working as a spy during World War II. But he partly got the idea for Bond after meeting a Serbian spy named Dusan Popov. Popov was a wealthy playboy and ladies' man who worked as a successful secret agent for Great Britain. He spoke several languages fluently and even developed his own recipe for invisible ink. But best of all was Popov's secret spy code name: *Tricycle*!

use a cell phone. Instead, he prefers to make secret rubber band messages. To do this, Hans stretches a rubber band around a book. He then writes his secret message on the rubber band with a pen. ("Nemesis on the move. Prepare water balloons!") To communicate his secret message, Hans takes the rubber band off the book and shoots it at me. This hurts, but at least I get the message. As the rubber band pulls back to its original size, the message disappears.

Although this rubber-band trick seems ingenious, it is actually a take-off on a technique that Alexander the Great's spies used around 340 BCE. (They would write on narrow scrolls wrapped around a stick. Unwinding the scroll broke up the words of the message until it was re-rolled.) Yes, it turns out that spies have been around for thousands of years. The first one was apparently a caveman who stole both the idea of the wheel AND a really good fig newton recipe.

AND ABOUT 2500 YEARS AGO, A CHINESE LEADER NAMED SUN TZU WROTE IN HIS FAMOUS BOOK THE ART OF WAR THAT "AN ARMY WITHOUT SECRET AGENTS IS LIKE A MAN WITHOUT EYES AND EARS."

Here are a few more tips on how *not* to get noticed while you're "out in the field." (No, not an actual field . . . unless your Nemesis is a llama.) First, don't make sudden movements as you skulk. If you're diving into doorways, everyone will notice you. Don't move your whole head when tracking your Nemesis. From a distance, he'll be able to see this. Instead, use just your eyes, and look near your target, but avoid making eye contact with him. If you can follow your Nemesis's progress by following his reflection in windows, do so.

Your appearance is important. Don't wear white shoes, and don't wear clothes that contrast with each other, like a white shirt with a dark jacket. Try to dress generically. Baseball hats are fine, but since the idea is to let the brim cover your face, don't put it on sideways or backward. Just try to fit in and act normal. In a library? Carry a book. In an animal feed store? Carry a pig.

Ah, but what if you think *you're* being followed? Just try turning around a lot as you walk. Crossing the street gives you a good chance to see your surroundings. Entering a store with large glass windows can give you a good lookout; be sure to watch the doorway. Some agents "accidentally" drop a piece of paper to see if someone else picks it up, but I've found this is also a good way to get in trouble for littering.

IN ORDER TO MAXIMIZE YOUR SPYING EFFICIENCY, YOU WILL NEED TO FORM A DEDICATED TEAM OF SPECIALISTS.

Of course, you will need to pay them, so first get a good job and start earning large amounts of money. Then, as you can afford them, put your team together with these roles in mind:

BREAK-IN EXPERT: This employee is good at "surreptitious entry." Be sure to hire someone who can pick locks, disarm burglary systems, and sweet-talk Doberman Pinschers. (Be careful not to get a Break-Out Expert; he will spend all day trying to get the high score on video games.)

DOUBLE AGENT: Although this person will *seem* to be working for you, he or she will actually be faithfully reporting back to your Nemesis! (I know this sounds inefficient, but take it from an expert: this is the way spy work works.)

CRYPTOLOGIST: This specialist will be able to crack whatever code your Nemesis is using, especially that hard-to-read one called "crummy handwriting." Put this person in charge of figuring out who crept into the crypt, crapped, and then crept out again. (My, that is funny.)

UTILITY INFIELDER: It's important to have someone around who can do a little of everything. This person can play catcher, shortstop, and first, second, or third base. That means if someone goes down with an injury, you can still field a team! (Oh wait, I'm sorry, wrong list.)

AS YOU AND YOUR TEAM LEARN YOUR NEMESIS'S DARKEST SECRETS, YOU MAY BE AMUSED, SURPRISED, OR EVEN DISGUSTED.

If you feel that the world would be a better place without your Nemesis around, you might consider assassination. Let me warn you against this, as it is apparently illegal.

Another possibility is "sabotage," which is trying to gain an advantage for yourself by destroying something. Sadly, sabotage is also frowned upon by society. So while laying explosives on your archenemy's rollerblading course seems like a good idea, my lawyer advises me it's actually not.

At this point you may feel somewhat frustrated. It seems like every time you turn around, law enforcement officials and other "do-gooders" are there waving you off. Perhaps what you need is a visit to Mischief Spy Camp! You will find registration information for it concealed elsewhere in this book.

ONE OF THE THINGS MY STAFF WILL TEACH YOU IS HOW TO RECRUIT SPIES TO YOUR TEAM. WITH OUR TRAINING, YOU WILL EVENTUALLY BE ABLE TO TURN THE FRIENDS AND FAMILY OF YOUR NEMESIS AGAINST HIM.

In fact, with techniques including blackmail, e-mail, and even Instant Messaging, it is even possible to turn your Nemesis against *himself*.

We will also instruct you in the fine art of wearing disguises. Rinky-dink operations encourage their agents to wear things like reversible jackets so that they can quickly change their "look." We take that idea one step further. Two words: *reversible underwear*. You'll also learn other excellent disguise costumes, including:

THE VEGETARIAN PIRATE: Who'd suspect anyone singing, "Ho, ho, ho, and a bottle of wheat grass juice"?

THE JANITOR: Have coveralls, will spy! (Campers must supply own mop.)

"THE MATRIX" REFUGEE: A trenchcoat and dark glasses? It's so clichéd, people will assume that you're either a Goth wannabe or the world's only member of the Keanu Reeves Fan Club.

It is also possible to change the way you walk. We suggest that you put a pebble in one shoe and a slice of Swiss cheese (cheddar also works) in the other. As your feet go through strange new sensations, you will find yourself walking with a new, disguised gait.

For phone conversations from public phones or borrowed cells, it is also possible to disguise your voice. Don't try to fake an accent; you will just sound like yourself trying to fake an accent.

Instead, take a pen or pencil and put it between your teeth. This will change your speech enough to fool whoever is on the other line, even if it's the greatest spy of all time.

Despite your cleverness, there may come a time when you are caught by enemy henchmen. That means you will have to fight your way out of a tough situation. Luckily, you will learn at camp that there are many everyday objects that can

The Greatest Spy of All Time

The legend of super spy Chad Borr has become shrouded in mystery. What is known about him is that he scorned double-agents as unambitious twits. As a result, Chad was a "quintuple agent," and to this day, nobody knows who he was really working for! Known as "the man without a face," the secret to Chad's success was simple: *he had no face*. As a result, most people had trouble identifying him and he was never caught.

assist you in combat. For example, you can whittle a breadstick down to a sharp point. Then you can jab the sharpened breadstick at your enemy's face! Or you can quickly hand your opponent a large jawbreaker. Make your escape while he sucks away.

IF YOU ALLOW YOURSELF TO BE CAPTURED, REMEMBER TO USE A GOOD ALIBI. OF COURSE, THIS MEANS YOU MAY BE CAUGHT IN AN UNTRUTH, BUT DON'T LET THAT STOP YOU. SHOULD THIS HAPPEN DURING A BRUTAL INTERROGATION SESSION ("NOT ANOTHER WET WILLIE!"), TRY QUOTING WINSTON CHURCHILL: "IN WARTIME, TRUTH IS SO PRECIOUS THAT SHE SHOULD ALWAYS BE ATTENDED BY A BODYGUARD OF LIES."

Mischief

OF THE RICH AND FAMOUS

"MISCHIEF IS A MOST PROFOUND PLEASURE." —*Frank Herbert*

Many (maybe even most!) of the leaders and famous (or infamous) people in history were mischief makers. They were the brave women who looked at how unfair the world was and said, "I can do better than that." They were the stalwart men who saw stupidity and asked, "Why do we have to do it that way?" And they were the delightful children who ganged up on the neighborhood bully and hit him with wet noodles until he said, "Uncle!"

YES, IT HAS BEEN HISTORY'S MISCHIEF MAKERS WHO HAVE HAD THE COURAGE TO POINT OUT THINGS LIKE SLAVERY, GLOBAL WARMING, AND TURTLENECK SWEATERS ARE BAD.

And these are also the people who pulled off some of the greatest hoaxes and practical jokes of all time. Their achievements include the Boston Tea Party, the "War of the Worlds" radio broadcast of 1938, and the Cheese Whiz Disaster of 2008.

In fact, if you look hard enough, you'll see that mischief makers perform services that we never thought about before, even when they don't mean to. For example, hackers try to make trouble by sneaking into other people's computers and programs. This is very, very wrong! But by doing so, the hackers let everyone know about weaknesses that exist in their computer security systems. That means the hackers are performing a valuable service for free!

So this chapter is devoted to some of the

most mischievous wisenheimers who believed that if you can't laugh at yourself, try laughing at others instead.

JACK NICHOLSON is a famous actor who supposedly has a clear plastic toilet seat at his house. Inside of it is coiled a large dead rattlesnake. This makes sitting down an exercise in bravery.

MOLLY IVINS was a writer who used her newspaper column to have fun and make fun. Molly thought that there were two kinds of humor. One was the kind that made people laugh about the mistakes that we all make and share. "The other kind holds people up to public contempt and ridicule," Molly said. "That's what I do." But Molly made it a rule to only mock important people. "When you use satire against powerless people," she said, "it is like kicking a cripple."

Ivins especially liked to write about Texas. When politicians from all over the state got together for meetings, Molly wrote that "every village is about to lose its idiot." And here she is writing about a foolish congressman: "If his IQ slips any lower, we'll have to water him twice a day." Ivins so hated the city of Dallas, she described it as a place "that would have rooted for Goliath to beat David."

In 1776, *GEORGE WASHINGTON* was preparing to cross

Butterfingers and Beaujolais

The older a fine wine is, the more expensive it is. In 1989, a wine merchant tried to sell a bottle of wine from 1787 (it had once been owned by Thomas Jefferson) for over $500,000. Holding the bottle up to show it off, the wine merchant dropped it. The bottle broke. *No sale!*

the Delaware River. (There is a famous painting of this trip.) Getting into his boat, Washington was concerned to see a heavy man named Henry Knox onboard. Washington said, "Shift that fat a**, Harry. But slowly, or you'll swamp the boat!"

THE MYTHBUSTERS are Jamie Hyneman, Adam Savage, and Peter Rees. These guys created a TV show where they take urban legends and put them to the test. It takes a special person to answer questions like: Can a microwaved jawbreaker explode in your mouth? (Yes.) Does quicksand actually suck you under and drown you? (No.) Can people row fast enough to pull a water skier? (Yes.) Would a penny dropped from the Empire State Building kill someone? (Nope.) Can you learn something while watching these guys blow things up? (Yes!)

Special bonus score: To Jamie Hyneman, for saying, "We take large objects and make them into very small objects."

JACK "LEGS" DIAMOND was an American gangster in the 1920s who survived many shoot-outs with rival criminals and the police. This led him to brag, "The bullet

hasn't been made that can kill me."

Diamond was shot to death not long after that.

ANDRE BRÉTON was a French artist and mischief maker. Before he died, Bréton made arrangements for his body to be taken to the graveyard in a moving van.

EDDIE HASKELL was the fictional neighbor kid on the TV show *Leave It To Beaver* (1958–1963). Eddie was sarcastic, sneaky, two-faced, and a born mischief maker. As June Cleaver said, "Eddie has that look about him that makes you think something's always about to happen." In fact, Matt Groening—the creator of *The Simpsons*—based the character of Bart Simpson on Eddie Haskell. Eddie was the kind of guy who would kiss up to your parents, and then when they turned their backs he would start picking on you. But the oily Eddie also hatched some fairly creative schemes. And most importantly, he usually got someone else

119

to actually carry out these ideas. Brilliant! (Of course, since it was an old-time TV show, Eddie's schemes never actually worked, but at least he tried.)

Special bonus score: For saying, "Wally, if your dumb brother tags along, I'm gonna—oh, good afternoon, Mrs. Cleaver. I was just telling Wallace how pleasant it would be for Theodore to accompany us to the movies."

PORKY BICKAR lived in Sitka, Alaska, where he led a band of mischief makers called the Dirty Dozen. Sitka is thirteen miles from a volcano that everyone thought was dormant. But in 1974, people woke up to see black smoke billowing out of it! Was it going to blow? Was Sitka going to be buried in lava? Gadzooks!

It turned out that Porky and his friends had flown into the volcano's crater and built a large fire. This was the smoke that gave everyone a shock. When Mount St. Helens exploded some years later, someone angrily erupted at him, saying, "This time you've gone too far!"

While faking an emergency is not funny and usually illegal, I'm willing to make an exception in this case.

Special bonus score: His name was Porky.

GERHARD ZUCKER was a German rocket scientist who developed small rockets that he thought would be useful for mail delivery. Gehard was able to persuade folks in the United Kingdom to try his idea, and in 1934, a mail rocket with 1,200 envelopes in it blasted off for mail delivery in Scotland.

The rocket blew up.

Despite this, the United States Postal Service also took a shot at Zucker's idea. In 1959, the Navy replaced the warhead on a nuclear missile with mail containers. Missile mail! A Navy submarine then shot the missile, which landed safely

and without a nuclear explosion, which is always nice.

United States Postmaster General Arthur Summerfield was very impressed with missile mail. He said, "Before man reaches the moon, mail will be delivered within hours from New York to California, to Britain, to India or Australia by guided missiles. We stand on the threshold of rocket mail."

Uh-huh.

Experiments with mail-delivery rockets have continued, but between the cost of missile mail and the chance for disaster, it seems unlikely that this idea will ever really take off.[1]

LEWIS GORIN was a college student in 1936 who wanted to have some fun while making an antiwar statement. So Lewis formed a group called the Veterans of Future Wars. The VFW was made up of young people who hadn't been to war yet, but probably would have to someday. The VFW grew to have tens of thousands of members, but some people didn't like them very much. National Commander James E. Van Zandt said, "They're too yellow to go to war. . . . They'll never be veterans of a future war." The commander was wrong; all the group's original members (including Gorin) ended up serving in World War II.

---

1. The rocket scientists at NASA sometimes get stuck on a hard math problem. Often, one of them will say, "How hard could this be? It's not rocket science." Then someone else will say, "Actually, it is!" Then they all laugh.

JOSEPH MERLIN invented roller skates in 1760. Wanting to show off his latest creation, Joseph wore his new roller skates to a fancy masquerade ball. While he was rolling around and impressing everyone, he lost his balance and smashed into an expensive mirror. Severely injured, he then got blood all over everything and everyone. Despite looking way uncool, both Joseph and his invention survived.

Our Coolest President?

When Calvin Coolidge was president of the United States (1923–1929), he liked to ring the front door of the White House and then run and hide when the servants answered it.

LOKI was an O.G.[2] when it came to making mischief. The Vikings worshipped a number of gods (like Thor!), and Loki was the main troublemaker among them. No prank was too big for Loki, so sometimes he took things a little too far, like when he killed Baldur or tried to destroy the entire universe. As Lore Sjöberg wrote, "If you think 'trickster' . . . you don't think of leading the legions of hell against the gods at the end of the universe, but that's exactly what Loki's got jotted down on his celestial PalmPilot."

PRESIDENT FRANKLIN D. ROOSEVELT always suspected that when people met him, they were too nervous meeting the president to actually listen to what he said. To test his

_____

2. Original god.

125

theory, FDR repeatedly said to guests meeting him at a reception, "I murdered my grandmother this morning."

Nobody said a word about it. They all just smiled politely and shook his hand!

Special bonus score: FDR was so superstitious, he would never leave for a trip on the thirteenth day of the month. If he had to, he would depart on 11:50 p.m. on the twelfth, or wait until 1:00 a.m. on the fourteenth. As you can imagine, this caused a lot of trouble.

Demerit: FDR's mom made him wear a dress until he was five.

THOMAS GRASSO was convicted of murder and sentenced to death in the 1990s. For his last meal, he requested SpaghettiOs. While Grasso did get spaghetti for his last meal, it was not the kind he asked for. Thomas Grasso's last words were, "I did not get my SpaghettiOs."

NICK FLYNN proved to the world that sometimes you can make a lot of trouble just by forgetting to tie your shoelaces. In 2006, Nick was visiting a museum in England that had three priceless antique vases on display. Taking a peek at them, Nick tripped on his untied shoelaces . . . and fell into the vases, knocking them over and smashing them to bits!

KURT VONNEGUT JR. was a famous author known for his black humor and creativity. As a college student, Vonnegut practiced a prank where he would go into a lecture hall during finals week and pick up a copy of the exam. Vonnegut would look the test over and then tear it up into little pieces right in the face of the professor.

Then he would storm out of class.

Of course, Vonnegut only did this in classes he was not enrolled in!

ERIK KING is my younger brother, and he is also a mischief maker. Like many mischief makers, Erik has a big ego. For example, when I was a kid, I used to sign my name "Bart the Great." (I think we can all agree that this was a fair and accurate description.) Unfortunately, Erik noticed what I was doing, and he started signing his name "Erik the Greater." That little jerk!

BUT BOTH OF US COULD HAVE LEARNED SOMETHING FROM HEAVYWEIGHT BOXING CHAMPION MUHAMMAD ALI, WHO SAID, "I AM NOT THE GREATEST; I AM THE DOUBLE-GREATEST."

It's hard to beat that.

JONATHAN SWIFT was a writer who loved to trick people to get them to think about the world in a different way. For example, Swift once wrote a satire called "A Modest Proposal." In it, he argued that feeding poor children to rich people had many advantages.[3] Of course, Swift didn't

---

3. Swift wrote, "A young healthy child well nursed is at a year old a most delicious, nourishing, and wholesome food."

actually think cannibalism was a good idea, but by pretending he did, he was able to show how cruel rich people could be to the poor.

In 1708, an astrologer named John Partridge predicted that a disease would sweep through London in early April, killing thousands of people. Annoyed by this stupidity, Swift wrote a pamphlet predicting that John Partridge would die on March 29! Then, right after March 29, Swift released another pamphlet confirming that Partridge had died, just as he had predicted.

So on April 1 (April Fools' Day), people came to Partridge's home, asking where his body was and where the funeral would be held. And although Partridge came to the door and tried hard to convince people that he was still alive, many would not believe it. After all, everyone knew he was dead!

Special bonus score: In Swift's book

Gulliver's Travels, the title character puts out a palace fire in the tiny land of Lilliput by peeing on it.

In 1856, serial murderer *WILLIAM PALMER* looked at the gallows he would be hanged on and asked, "Are you sure this thing is safe?

BELVA ANN LOCKWOOD became one of the first female lawyers in the United States. She did this even though a judge once told her, "Women are not needed in the courts. Their place is in the home to wait upon their husbands, to bring up the children, to cook the meals, make beds, polish pans and dust furniture." Belva said the heck with that. She went on to run for president of the United States twice, even though women were not even allowed to vote at the time.

Special bonus score: Belva rode around Washington, D.C., on a large tricycle. (Really.)

Double bonus score: Her name was Belva.

NICOLO FRANCO lived in Italy back in the 1500s. He made the mistake of writing graffiti on a bathroom wall. But how mad could anyone get over a little tagging? Well, Nicolo was visiting a luxurious new bathroom in the Vatican that the pope had requested. Amazed at how wonderful the bathroom was, Nicolo wrote on the wall, "Pope Pius. . . has erected this noble monument of caca seats." The pope didn't find this very funny, and Nicolo was hanged.

131

NERO (37–68 BCE) was one of the worst rulers that ancient Rome ever got stuck with. Nero was convinced that he was a genius, and he was greatly saddened that the world would have to go on without him. His last words: "What an artist dies with me!"

THOMAS BAKER was a missionary who traveled to the South Pacific island of Fiji. While there in 1867, he was seized by a group of Fijians. To calm his group's fears that their captors were not cannibals, Baker said, "Fijians are not lovers of human flesh." One of the Fijians later reported that "we ate everything but his boots."

A PARACHUTIST WITH A STICK OF DYNAMITE made news in 1973. That was the year that six hundred thousand people (a world record!) gathered for a rock concert called Summer Jam in upstate New York. To amaze and impress the concert-goers, a daredevil decided to parachute out of a plane above them. He would then light and throw a stick of dynamite that would explode loudly but harmlessly far above their heads.

As the plane swooped over the crowd, the parachutist got ready. He checked his equipment, and then he lit the fuse on the dynamite and jumped! As he fell, he threw the dynamite. Oops . . . he didn't think to consider that the dynamite would fall at the exact same speed he fell! Frantically, he reached for his ripcord to open his chute, and then there was a huge explosion.

What was left of the parachutist floated gently down into the crowd of concert-goers. (There was no encore.)

GEORGE CLOONEY once supposedly played a little prank on a friend who had cats. George supposedly busted a grumpy in the cats' litter box when his friend wasn't around. To appreciate the genius of this, imagine his friend's reaction when he saw George's gift.

George Clooney is my hero.

Just south of Kazakhstan (where Borat is from!) there was once a massive empire called Khwarezmia. In the early 1200s, Khwarezmia was the richest empire in the world. But its ruler, *SHAH ALLAH AL-DIN MUHAMMAD II* (aka the Shah), destroyed his fabulously wealthy kingdom with a bad practical joke.

The Shah was annoyed because the Mongols had their own large empire growing to the east of Khwarezmia. So when the Mongol leader Genghis Khan sent two Mongol leaders to the capital of Khwarezmia, the Shah got an idea for a "joke." Everyone knew that the Mongols never, ever shaved their beards. So the Shah thought it would be funny to have his guards seize the Mongols and shave off all their whiskers (and hair!) The bare-faced Mongols were then sent back to Genghis Khan.

Genghis was not amused. In 1219, he sent a Mongol army to destroy the Shah's empire. Within a year, the army had killed three to four million people, and the Khwarezmian empire was gone.

All because the Shah decided to play a little joke.[4]

Today, the Shah stands as a painful reminder to us that timing and good judgment are all-important when it comes to mischief making.

_____

4. As for the Shah, the Mongols chased him for two thousand miles, but before they could capture him, the Shah died from the shame of playing the worst prank in the history of the world. As Chinua Achebe wrote, "A man who makes trouble for others is also making trouble for himself."

Also, it can be impossible to undo something foolish that you have done.

And finally, it's usually not a good idea to pick a Mongol in charge of huge armies as your Nemesis.

Inspired

BY THE OXFORD
DICTIONARY

*"NO MAN IS EXEMPT FROM SAYING
SILLY THINGS; THE MISCHIEF IS TO
SAY THEM DELIBERATELY."*
—Michel de Montaigne

The Oxford Dictionary of English states
that there are 350 useful one-word insults
in English. Even better, many more
words can be creatively mixed to become
friendly insults. The people of Scotland
have a particularly rich tradition here.
That's because the Scots once had a tradition at the royal court called "flyteing."
Poets practiced complex insults and then

used them in the court as entertainment for the big shots. And so today, the Scots can choose from a wide number of insults like *nyaff* (a good-for-nothing), *ned* (non-educated delinquent), and *numpty* (an absent-minded person). And those are just ones that start with "n"!

Study and memorize the following fabulous words. You'll never use an actual cuss word again! And if anyone complains when you use them, explain that they are just "sentence enhancers." And who could be against enhanced sentences?

BEZONIAN: A troublemaker.

BLACKGUARD: A cheater or troublemaker.

BLUDGER (AUSTRALIAN): A lazy person.

BLUNTIE (BLUN-TEE): Scottish term for a dumb person: "He is not keen or sharp; he's a bluntie!"

BOGOSITY: The state of being bogus.

BOOFHEAD (AUSTRALIAN): Silly but nice person.

BROMIDROSIS: Stinky sweat: "Good grief, look at those pit stains! And even worse, you have bromidrosis!"

CEPACEOUS: Looking like an onion.

CLOT: Someone who is a lump.

COCKALORUM: A little squirt who thinks he's a big shot.

DANDIPRAT: A silly person.

DIDYMITIS: An infection of the private parts.

DIPHTHONG: This is actually the sound of two vowels (as in "coin"), but I think it works as an insult as well.

DRONGO (AUSTRALIAN): Idiot.

ENCOPRESIS: To accidentally go poop, usually in one's pants.

Vocabulary Warning: Bad Good Words!

Scientists often try to find the most beautiful words in the English language. These are important to know because a mischief maker has no business using words like these. For us, these are the bad words. *Blech!*

The following words came from a survey of 35,000 English speakers and some language experts who found these to be the most wonderful-sounding words ever. Avoid them all!

mother	mist	blue
smile	whisper	sunflower
love	rainbow	lullaby
blossom	liberty	cute
sunshine	peace	melody
fantastic	sweetheart	cozy
butterfly	gorgeous	bubble
destiny	velvet	giggle
freedom	enthusiasm	diarrhea[1]
dawn	hope	chinchilla

FLOCCULENT: Covered with tufts of wool.

FOPDOODLE: A chowderhead.

GALAH (AUSTRALIAN): A loud-mouthed nitwit. (This comes from the name for a loud Australian bird.)

GOWK: Simpleton.

HEBETUDINOUS: Lethargic; dull

HOME-SCHOOLED: A person, situation, or object that is lame. As home-schoolers are often the brightest kids around, I know this is an unfair usage. But as public school students know, life is not always fair.

LARDY-DARDY (BRITISH): A boy who cares a little too much about his clothes.

LURDANE: Boring and lazy.

MACULATION: Covered in spots.

---

1. Okay, you can use this one.

MOMO: Someone who is irritating.

MOUTH BREATHER: A foolish person who never closes his or her mouth; aka slackjaw.

MUCOPHAGOUS: Booger eating.

MUCOPURULENT (MYOO-KO-PUR-YOO-LENT): Containing a mix of mucus and pus.

MUCUS TROOPER: Someone who is mucophagous.

MUFFIN TOP: The roll of fat that spills over the top of tight pants. "Untuck your shirt so we don't have to see your muffin top."

MUPPET: An ignorant person who has no original ideas.

NIDDERING: Cowardly.

PLANK: Someone as smart as a plank of wood.

Quick Mischief

★ If a colleague or classmate is going on vacation, disconnect his or her keyboard. Spread some alfalfa seeds on it. Cover the seeds with a moist paper towel. Then slip the whole keyboard into a big Ziploc bag and leave it unsealed. Just before your victim comes back, pull the keyboard out (it will be covered in alfalfa sprouts) and put it back where it was. Then look innocent!

POTLICKER: A fishing term that describes someone who steals good fishing spots, but it can be used for anyone who sneaks in on what isn't theirs.

PROTO-HUMAN: A primitive form of a person, not really human at all.

SCHMUCK: Silly goof.

SMATCHET: A small, nasty person.

THUMBSUCKER: No explanation needed. Extra credit to anyone who says *fumbshucker*.

The Underworld

The Viking god of mischief, Loki, had a daughter who was black on one side and white on the other. Here name was Hel, and her kingdom was Niflheim. This was the underworld, where Vikings believed most souls went after they died. Although Niflheim wasn't all that bad, Hel's name later came to be associated with a very unpleasant place. In fact, after someone added an "l" to her name, her name became a bad word for some people!

If you are looking to refer to H-E-Double-Hockey-Sticks but don't want to actually say it, here are some alternatives:

★ the abyss
★ Avernus
★ the bottomless pit
★ Brimstone Land
★ Detroit
★ Erebus
★ Gehenna
★ Hades
★ Las Vegas
★ the Nether World
★ perdition
★ the pit of Acheron
★ Sheol
★ Stygia
★ Tartarus
★ the void

TOXIC SOCK SYNDROME: Stinky socks.

TUKHES (TOOK-HIS): The Yiddish word for "butt."

URINIFEROUS (YOOR-IN-IF-ER-US): Carrying pee or urine.

VERRUCOSE: Covered in warts.

WAZZOCK (ENGLISH): Mild insult for someone who is foolish.

WHIFFLE: A pipsqueak, a twerp.

Let me caution you against writing Poison Pen letters to your Nemesis. While it can be tempting to put some of the new words you've learned into writing, there is a special word used for the kind of letter you are thinking of: EVIDENCE.

But if you can't restrain yourself, put your Poison Pen away and use your Nontoxic Pen to write something inoffensive, anonymous, and silly. This will confound your enemy much more than a sheet full of insults. For example:

Dear You,

On the day that you were born, the angels got together and decided to create a dream come true. Okay, I got that from a song, but it's how I feel about you, wonderful you! I'm too shy to let you know who this is (and you'll never guess), so just know that I'm not alone. Lots of people would like to follow you around everywhere. Just like me, they long to be close to you.

Signed,

?????????

International Mischief

What country in the world is the most athletic? I'm not sure, but if we focus on Europe, it could be Poland, which hosts the World Screaming Championships. Or perhaps Sweden, which has the Snowball Throwing Contest. Finland is also a strong candidate. It has the Air Guitar World Championships, the World Wife-Carrying Championships (men pick up their wives and race about three hundred yards), and the World Mosquito-Killing Contest.

But the winner is . . . the United Kingdom! There spectators can choose to watch the World Bog Snorkeling Championship (snorkeling in a muddy swamp), the Biggest Liar in the World Championship, or the Cooper's Hill Cheese Rolling Contest (athletes chase a giant round cheese down a hill). But nothing can compare to the thrill of the World Gurning Championship. "Gurning" means "to make a horrible face." So for this event, contestants come out and grimace, grin, leer, and otherwise contort their visages into the ugliest shapes possible. Sweet!

Although it's on the wrong continent, the United States gets honorable mention for hosting the Ultimate Couch Potato Contest. Whoever can sit on a couch the longest while watching TV wins a forty-two-inch television. (How do you cheer for that? "Watch! Watch! Keep . . . watching . . . Zzzzzzz.") And the United States also has the Summer Redneck Games, where hubcap hurling and spitball bug zapping are official events. But few events can match the Sludge Olympics. Also known as the Sewage Treatment Olympics, this is where sewage workers from across the nation compete in events like fixing broken sewer pipes and saving people who have been knocked out by noxious gases.

What's in a Name?

The people of Venezuela have gotten in the habit of being very mischievous with words—they often give their children very unusual names. These names might be imported ("Elvis Presley" and "Taj Mahal" are popular choices) or they might be a combination of the parents' names. So if a man named Nelson and

Spring Back, Fall Forward?

The way that we use words helps to determine how we think. For example, there are people who live in the mountains of South America who speak a language called Aymara. In this language, the way to say "future" is to say "behind time." And the way to say "past" is "front time." Because what happens in the past is known, it lies in *front* of you. You can see what happened. But the future is unknown, so it is *behind* you, where it is invisible! This is the opposite viewpoint of almost every other culture and language on the planet. My conclusion: speakers of Aymara are mischief makers! (And pretty smart, too.)

a woman named Marta have a son, he might be named "Nelmar." But what if your dad was named Dwayne and your mom was named Habeeb?[1]

---

1. Your name would be Dweeb.

Venezuelan names also come from another name spelled backwards. So both "Hector" and "Rotceh" are common names, as is "Aleuzenev." Novelist Roberto Echeto says that for Venezuelans, naming their babies "is an almost irresistible invitation to rebel against centuries of tradition." *¡Viva la revolución!*

Sweden is in northern Europe, which is generally known as Scandinavia. This is where the Vikings used to dwell, and they had some interesting ideas about names as well. A nice girly-girl name for the Vikings was Skadi, which means "damage." And a boy might go by the name Gunnar, which translates to "war warrior." The Vikings gave their slaves even worse names. One Viking poem tells of slave characters known as Clump, Thicklegs, and Foul. And when Vikings explored eastern Canada about a thousand years ago, they named the Native Americans they met *skraelings*, or "wretch dwarves." That's not very nice!

(IT WAS ALSO NOT VERY NICE OF MY PARENTS TO GIVE ME A WEIRD MIDDLE NAME: ALGAE. YES, I AM BART ALGAE KING.)

In the United States, when we write or say a person's name, the family name goes last, and the first name goes, uh, first. In China, this order is reversed! A person's family name comes *first*. And there aren't that many Chinese family names out there. Almost 90 percent of Chinese people share about a hundred family names. To make up for this, parents sometimes give their kids unique personal names. For instance, in 2007, a Chinese couple named their kid @ (pronounced "at," which sounds like the Chinese phrase "love him.") If @ ever gets lost, people can ask, "Where is @ at?" And if he tattles on other kids, he could be nicknamed "Rat-a-tat-t@." And little baby @ might get a weird e-mail address later in life; he might be @@gmail.com.

In China, because of superstition, it's also a custom to call a newborn baby a "stinky little pig." This name is supposed to fool evil spirits that might otherwise bother the child. (I guess evil spirits are not too bright!)

Name problems can happen when people translate from other languages to English. For example, a Japanese man named Miyamoto invented the video game Donkey Kong in the 1980s. If you've ever played the game, you know there is no donkey. But the game does have a very stubborn gorilla that keeps kidnapping a girl named Pauline from her boyfriend. Miyamoto wanted to name his game something like "stubborn gorilla." He finally came up with "Donkey Kong" because he knew donkeys were stubborn, and he figured it would be obvious what he meant.

WHEN THE NINTENDO PEOPLE IN THE UNITED STATES HEARD THE NAME, THEY THOUGHT IT WAS SILLY, BUT THEY WENT WITH DONKEY KONG ANYWAY. AND THE DESPITE THE ODD TITLE, THE GAME HAS BEEN A HUGE HIT.

What's the worst name ever? Enrique II (1334–1379) wanted to be the ruler of the Spanish kingdom so badly, he murdered his own brother to get the crown. This didn't go over well with Enrique's new subjects, who nicknamed the new king "El Bastardo." Nice.

Red Scare

Nicholas I (1796–1855) was a Russian ruler who was so mean, he once had a group of men arrested for reading books and having conversations. The czar wanted to teach his prisoners[2] a lesson. So Russian soldiers took the prisoners into a public square where they were told they would be shot.

Thousands of people gathered as the group's death sentence was read aloud. The prisoners were blindfolded and their hands were tied. The members of the firing squad raised their

2. Who included Fyodor Dostoyevsky, the author of *Crime and Punishment* and *The Idiot*.

rifles. The tension was so thick you could cut it with a butter knife!

Suddenly, a galloping horse carried a soldier into the square. "Stop!" the soldier cried. (The horse maintained a dignified silence.) The soldier explained that the whole thing was just a joke to scare the prisoners. They weren't going to be shot after all!

The men slumped in relief.

"Instead," the soldier explained, "you're all going to work camps in Siberia!"

Czar Nicholas thought this was hilarious.

Mischievous Foods

Maybe you think that food has no role in mischief making. (After all, what's funny about a ham sandwich? *Nothing*.) But Australian comedian Barry Humphries, who has played many excellent food pranks, disagrees. For instance, here's a food trick he likes to do while working with a team. Barry gets on a commuter train, and at the first stop, a friend gets on and silently gives him a grapefruit on a plate. Barry eats it, and at the next stop, another friend gets on, takes the grapefruit rind, and gives Barry a bowl of cornflakes. At the next stop, Barry is given bacon and eggs by another rider. To the amazement of his fellow commuters, he ends up eating a complete multicourse breakfast in this fashion.

Barry has also been known to put a nice meal in a bag and then put the bag in a garbage can near a bus stop or other place where people gather regularly. Barry later returns to the garbage can and rummages through it until he finds his bag. Then he

Space Chunks

NASA retired its famous "Vomit Comet" jet in 2004. This aircraft was used to train astronauts for zero gravity, and many an astronaut lost his cookies (and Tang!) onboard. Flight crews kept track of how much astronaut vomit they had to clean up over the years: over 280 gallons.

opens it and casually begins eating the food, to the amazement of spectators.

And on airplane flights, Barry sometimes brings "Russian salad" (diced vegetables in a mayonnaise sauce) with him onboard. He sneaks the salad into his barf bag as soon as he takes his seat. Later in the flight, he loudly pretends to actually barf into the same bag. With everyone looking, Barry then looks inside the bag, reaches in, and carefully starts eating his salad. Wow.

Five Fun Food Ideas

1. FROZEN JUICE: If your family drinks juice in the morning, try this trick. It will only work if you use nontransparent glasses at your house. Fill a cup halfway with juice before you go to bed. (You may have to do some juice concentrating to remember this.) Put it in the freezer. The next morning, top off the glass with regular juice and present it to your victim. The look on your half-asleep sister's face as she tries to figure out why her cup of juice won't come out will be worth the trouble.

2. *I SCREAM:* As you know, vanilla ice cream is white. Guess what? So is mayonnaise! Next time you're in the vicinity of a person who wants some vanilla ice cream, put a scoop of mayo at the bottom of his or her bowl or cone. Wait to see if it gets noticed! (I'm guessing it will.)

3. *HOLD (AND FREEZE) THE MAYO:* If you have a small jar of mayo you don't mind ruining, try this. Take your jar of mayonnaise and peel off its label. Then stick it in the freezer all day or all night . . . either way, let it freeze, come back later, and pull it out of the freezer. Now let it thaw out. When it's defrosted, take a look. Disgusting!

The mayo separates back into its original scientific ingredients: clear oil and oleaginous white stuff. (And there's a lot

THE POCKET GUIDE TO MISCHIEF

of oil.) Shake that jar really hard for a few minutes. Now take a look again. It's even more horrifying!

4. *RUSSIAN ROULETTE:* Get together a group of four or more people to enjoy some refreshing ice cream cones. But before eating anything, everyone in the group must agree to the following. You will all watch as someone puts ketchup and/or mustard in the bottom of one cone. You will all keep watching as ice cream goes on top of all the cones, including the one with condiments at the bottom. You will all look away as someone who is not playing "shuffles" the cones around. When the shuffling is complete, no one will know who is going to get the nasty cone, but it doesn't matter. The rules state *everyone* has to eat his or her *entire* cone. Mustard-y!

5. *DRESS FOR SUCCESS:* For this trick, you will need one of those small plastic champagne bottles that makes a loud little "pop!" when you pull the string out of the neck. Try taping one of these to the

bottom of a salad bowl. Pull the string up the bowl and into the salad. Odds are that someone will see the string and try to pull the string from the salad. There's a possibility that he or she will pull the string right out of the popper! Note: Only do this with a wooden salad bowl, as it's possible the surprised someone might knock the bowl off the table.

Restaurant Behavior

Is anything worse than eating at a restaurant where everyone is snooty and oh-so proper? Make your presence known right away. That way the waiter knows whom he's dealing with.

WHEN THE WATER ARRIVES, HOLD UP YOUR GLASS AND COMPLAIN, "HEY, MY WATER HAS BEEN DILUTED!" THIS SHOWS THAT YOU ARE A CUSTOMER WITH HIGH STANDARDS.

After looking over the menu, order a horse steak. When told that the restaurant

Quick Mischief

★ Replace Oreo cookie filling with Crisco or mint toothpaste.

★ Make a "sponge cake" by frosting a large sponge (the kind you use to wash a car.)

★ Bake cookies and show up to someone's house. Act like they invited you over.

★ Sprinkle powdered sugar under someone's bedsheets.

doesn't serve horses, whine and say, "But I'm so hungry, I could eat a horse." Then explain to the group and waiter in your most annoying, honor-student voice that it's been legal to eat horses in France since 1811, and horses are eaten in Japan and Sweden, too.

Next, consider the leg of lamb as an alternative, because it's a "sheep thrill" and there's "mutton like it." (The waiter will be laughing so hard, he'll swallow his gum.)

End by proclaiming that you have a beef with vegetarians: just because they're better than everyone else, they think that they're better than everyone else!

Then order the vegetarian plate.

At some point after the food arrives, encourage any small people with you (like children or grandparents with osteoporosis) to sit under the table where you can feed them table scraps. This is usually when the waiter, manager, or chef asks the eternal question "Is everything all right?" Since "everything" covers a lot of

May I Flush Your Order?

In Taiwan, a restaurant named Marton serves food to its diners in little toilet bowls, with both the Western flush and Eastern non-flush varieties. Diners order their food while seated on fake toilets, and urinals are mounted around the walls.

ground, this is a good time to comment on the restaurant's carpeting, the status of your bowels, and your thoughts on turtlenecks.

Of course, when you leave the restaurant, you will make up for your bad behavior by forking over a good tip. Waiters and waitresses have tough jobs, so find it in your heart to leave a tip that's around 20 percent of your bill. Of course, there is no law that you have to leave a tip, so if you got bad service, feel free to leave a tip that's about 0 percent of the bill.

Road Kill

An anonymous demented person[1] told me that his father practiced the following activity:

Create a costume that will make you look like a crazy hunchback or perhaps a wild

---

1. Jared Smith

ape man. This can be accomplished by wearing shoulder pads under a trench coat, maybe a fake wig and beard, or a Bill O'Reilly mask. Next, get a white stuffed animal (perhaps a rabbit) and a bottle of ketchup.

Find a spot near your house where you can emerge from shrubbery and be *seen* by passing traffic without being *run over* by passing traffic. At dusk, go to your hiding place in the shrubbery. Pour ketchup on

Frying in Your Own Fat Award

Marco Evaristti is an artist who lives in Chile. In 2007, Marco served dinner to friends at an art gallery. So what? Well, Marco gave his guests a dish of meatballs that had been cooked using fat that was liposuctioned from his own body. He claimed the meatballs were delicious and said, "You are not a cannibal if you eat art."

Nope, just an idiot!

the stuffed animal and toss it by the side of the road. Then emerge from the shrubs, lurching and acting spooky, and crouch over the "road kill." Make sure that you're facing traffic as you pretend to devour the stuffed animal. Remember to make horrible grimaces. You may want to consider shaking the animal in your mouth, like a dog with a toy.

If anyone stops his or her car, lurch back into the bushes while speaking in German. (If you don't know how to speak German, shout out the passages of this book that you have memorized. This will be just as incomprehensible to most people.)

Sporting Mischief

"IT IS NOT ENOUGH TO SUCCEED. OTHERS MUST FAIL."
—*Gore Vidal, noted author and athlete*

Sports rule. Cheaters stink. And there is no place for cheaters in sports.[1]

After all, everybody knows that cheating is wrong, and, of course, nobody wants to play with cheaters. (You know why? They cheat!) But once in a great while, cheating can result in something good.

---

1. Not counting professional athletes, of course.

For example, rugby is an excellent game that was supposedly invented by a kid named Will Ellis. In 1832, Will was playing soccer, and at some point, he just picked up the ball and started running with it. Cheater! Naturally, people started chasing Will and trying to take the ball away, and voilà, rugby was born. So today, rugby players can kick, gouge, push, and tackle because of a little cheater from long ago.

SPEAKING OF SOCCER, MY FAVORITE SOCCER STORY IS ABOUT A PROFESSIONAL EUROPEAN PLAYER NAMED STAF VAN DEN BUYS. IN THE MID-1990S, STAF SCORED THREE GOALS IN ONE GAME. UNFORTUNATELY, HE ACCIDENTALLY SCORED ALL HIS GOALS ON HIS OWN TEAM! STAF'S TEAM LOST BY A SCORE OF 3-2. OOPS!

---

2. Maybe Staf would have been better off using the kind of soccer ball people used back in the 1300s: a pig's head.

Maybe the most famous sport involving kicking, pushing, and sometimes even hair pulling was the gladiator contests in ancient Rome. Of course, everyone knows that the gladiators were forced to fight to the death. But did you know that there were different types of gladiators? You've probably seen pictures of the *retiarius*, the gladiators who carried a trident and a net. Less well-known are the *laquearii*, who tried to lasso their opponents, and the *andabata*, who had to fight using helmets with no eyeholes. Since they couldn't see, they were allowed to fight on horseback. (No, I am not making this up.) So the *andabata* fought (to the death!) while blind and on the back of a galloping horse. Thumbs up!

Sadly, the gladiator games were outlawed after a contestant stubbed his toe on a shield and sued the Roman Empire.

But today, Italy is still home to one of the world's greatest sporting events—the annual orange battle of Ivrea!

Ivrea is a city in northern Italy. Each year, thousands of people gather there for three days and they throw about a million oranges at each other. The sky is filled with citrus fruits raining down on the crowds. And yes, people wear lots and lots of protective gear, so nobody gets hurt, only sticky.

This festival began hundreds of years ago, back in the days when a noble could claim the right to spend the night with an engaged woman before her husband did. When the noble of Ivrea tried to use this right with a young woman named Violetta, she was not pleased. In fact, Violetta was so unhappy that she cut off his head and displayed it to the townsfolk from his castle balcony. The townsfolk got fired up, stormed the castle, and burned it down.

No oranges were involved.

In the years since, the people of Ivrea have continued to celebrate this triumph over the local meanie. Nowadays Ivrea's

#1 Fans

Yale University students posed as members of the "Harvard Pep Squad" before a football game in 2004. The tricksters handed out almost two thousand large cards to a group of Harvard fans. The fans were told that when each of the cards was lifted up, they would together spell "Go Harvard" in huge letters to the fans on the other side of the stadium.

In the second quarter, the pep squad told the fans to hold their cards up. The crowd did so, spelling out the words "We Suck" in huge letters! Since the Harvard fans couldn't see the message they were holding, they didn't realize they'd been tricked until after the game was over.

orange-throwing festival works on "symbolism." The oranges used in the battles are symbols for the head of the noble. The pulp and juice are his blood. And orange juice runs pulpy in the streets for three days of orange throwing!

Violetta would be proud.

Although throwing oranges is fun, not everyone has a chance to go to Ivrea. So what is the most competitive and exciting game that you could take part in near your home? To find out, a study of five major sports[3] measured which sport had the most upsets and the most unpredictable winners of each match. (In other words, what sport was the most exciting.) The winner? Soccer!

IN 1969, EL SALVADOR AND HONDURAS PLAYED A SOCCER GAME IN THE WORLD CUP TOURNAMENT. EL SALVADOR WON, AND FEELINGS BETWEEN THE TWO COUNTRIES WERE SO BAD THAT WAR WAS DECLARED TWO WEEKS LATER.

Football can be exciting too, and sometimes the thrills come before the game even starts. In 1896, Georgia Tech's college football team traveled by railroad to Auburn

---

3. Soccer, baseball, American football, basketball, hockey.

for a game. But when the conductor tried to stop the train at the station, it slipped along on the tracks for ten miles before finally halting. This was because Auburn students had greased the train tracks! Georgia Tech's team had to walk the ten miles back to the train station. Tired and grumpy, they lost the game to Auburn that day 45–0. (They gave up over four points for each mile they walked.)

If soccer or football is too exciting for you, there is always Rock, Paper, Scissors. This has recently become a professional sport, with thousands of dollars in prize money going to the best Rock, Paper,

Scissors athlete around. And here's a tip: according to champion player Jason Simmons, girls and women are much more likely to open with Scissors. Men open with Rock or Paper, but if they're left-handed, they may open with Scissors. Also, advanced players sometimes throw the same thing over and over to confuse their opponents. Like Bart Simpson says, "Good old Rock. Nothing beats Rock."

GET CREATIVE WITH OTHER VERSIONS OF ROCK, PAPER, SCISSORS! FOR EXAMPLE, YOU COULD ADD "BLACK HOLE" TO THE MIX BY MAKING AN "O" WITH YOUR THUMB AND FINGER. SINCE BLACK HOLES SUCK EVERYTHING INTO THEMSELVES, THEY ARE UNDEFEATABLE. "GOOD OLD BLACK HOLE. NOTHING BEATS BLACK HOLE."

If you don't have all the equipment you need to play Rock, Paper, Scissors, you may want to choose a simpler game, like perhaps a Spitting Contest. Spitting Contests usually revolve around who can spit the farthest. To make things more dramatic, contestants often spit off high places, like towers, bridges, or the top of a bunk bed. But be careful when you try to get that extra edge. In 2007, a German man having a spitting contest with a twelve-year-old boy accidentally threw himself out of a second-story window trying to give his spit a little extra momentum. How embarrassing is that? So be careful out there, you loogie hawkers.

Coaches

Anyone who has ever played a sport knows that coaches are fun people to be around. And when coaches take the game too seriously, they can be fun to make fun of! If you can't hold your tongue the next time your coach gives a pep talk that seems a little silly, here's a great idea:

COACH: "TO WIN, WE MUST REMEMBER THERE IS NO 'I' IN 'TEAM.'"

YOU (THOUGHTFULLY): "BUT THERE IS A 'ME!'"

Of course, sometimes the coach is actually a mischief maker as well. Take Andy Lipson, for example. Andy is a teacher in Portland, Oregon, who coached the basketball team that his son, Charlie, played on. In the fourth quarter of a close game, Charlie was fouled. He went to the free throw line, dribbled, and concentrated on the basket. As Charlie prepared to shoot, someone in the gym yelled loudly, "Air ball!"

After missing the shot, Charlie looked over to see who would have played such a cheap trick. It was his own dad, Andy! You know, the guy who was coaching Charlie's team?! Was Andy trying to make Charlie a little less nervous before

---

White House Hoops

Of the more than forty United States presidents, only three have been shorter than five feet seven inches.

---

a big shot? Nah! Was he trying to get a cheap laugh from the guys on the bench? Maybe! Was he a mischief maker who just couldn't help himself? Yes! With coaches like that, who needs books like this one?[4]

Mascots

What are the names of the teams that you play on or root for? Way back when, sports teams had fierce names that struck terror into their opponents' hearts, like the Vandals or the Pixies. For example, I went to a school known as the Warriors. The mascot was a Roman soldier with an upraised sword. Not bad!

But sensitive people decided that this was not a very nice mascot, and the Roman soldier was changed to a new mascot: a cedar tree. But seriously, this was a great choice because . . . you know . . . because

---

4. You do. And despite the missed free throw, Charlie's team won the game.

cedar trees are very competitive and tough. Plus, it's easy to *root* for a cedar tree, right? Right.

Still, the cedar tree is not as nice as Centenary College's mascot. Its women's teams are the Ladies and its men's teams are the Gentlemen. Yes, they're the Ladies and Gentlemen. But how do you root for them? "Go get 'em, Ladies and Gentlemen!"

But the all-time nicest mascot is probably the one for Southampton, a soccer team in England: Super Saint!

Some mascots are very odd indeed. For example, why do some teams have a mascot that has nothing to do with their

I Knew Something Was Wrong

Proof that golfers are insane: In New Zealand, peewee golf is called "crazy golf."

team name? For instance, the Phoenix Suns have a gorilla for a mascot, while the Philadelphia 76ers have Hip-Hop the Rabbit. English soccer mascots are just as odd. They range from the hopelessly lame, like Baggie the Bird (West Bromwich Albion), to the bizarre, like Robbie the Blobbie and Mr. Toffee (Bury, Everton).

But despite their cute names, these soccer mascots sometimes get in big trouble. For instance, Toby the Tyke (Barnsley) was lectured by police for using a toilet roll inappropriately in front of rival fans. And Wolfie (of Wolverhampton) once got in big trouble for fighting with Bristol City's Three Little Pigs![5]

Other interesting mascot categories include the following:

---

5. A wee bit north in Scotland, Hoopy the Huddle Hound (representing the local Celtics) was once arrested for picking people's pockets during a game.

Not Gonna Scare Anybody

ARTIE THE FIGHTING ARTICHOKE (Scottsdale Community College, Arizona)

BAMBIES
(St. Hubert High, Pennsylvania)

BEETDIGGERS (Jordan High, Utah)

DOTS (Poca High, West Virginia—they're the Poca Dots!)

LEMMINGS
(Bryant & Stratton College, Ohio)

MUD HENS
(Toledo, Ohio, minor league baseball)

POETS (Whittier College, California)

SYRUPMAKERS (Cairo High, Georgia)

WONDER BOYS (Arkansas Tech University, men's teams)

WOODEN SHOES
(*Teutopolis High, Illinois*)

Odd Invertebrates

BANANA SLUGS (*University of California–Santa Cruz*)

EARWIGS (*Las Olivas High, California*)

BLACK FLIES
(*College of the Atlantic, Maine*)

BOLL WEEVILS (*University of Arkansas–Monticello*)

Huh?

ICHABOD (*Washburn University, Kansas, men's teams*)[6]

---

6. Ichabod is a man dressed in early 1900s clothing, described as having "courage and enthusiasm, as shown by his brisk walk. He is . . . courteous, for he tips his hat as he passes . . . he studiously carries a book under his arm. His friendly smile makes you like him."

GORLOKS (Webster University, Missouri)

GREEN TERROR
(McDaniel College, Maryland)

MAGICIANS
(LeMoyne–Owen College, Tennessee)

MARTIANS (Goodrich High, Michigan)

ORPHANS (Centralia High, Idaho)

VULCANS (University of Hawai'i–Hilo)

Everyone Hates Them

LAWYERS (John Marshall High, Ohio)

MILLIONAIRES
(Williamsport High, Pennsylvania)

Fighting Fools

FIGHTING CAMELS
(Campbell University, North Carolina)

FIGHTING CHICKS
(*Chicasaw High, Oklahoma*)

FIGHTING JERSEYS
(*Falfurrias High, Texas*)

FIGHTING LEATHERNECKS
(*Western Illinois University*)

FIGHTING PLANETS
(*Mars Area High, Pennsylvania*)

The Coolest!

ATOM SMASHERS (*Johnson High, Georgia*)

CHEESE MAKERS (*Tillamook High, Oregon*)

CRIMINALS (*Yuma High, Arizona*)

DIRT BAGS (*California State University–
Long Beach, baseball*)

MANIACS (*Orofino High, Idaho*)

MASTODONS (*Indiana University–Purdue*

University Fort Wayne)

NIMRODS (Watersmeet High, Michigan)

STORMY THE ICE HOG (Carolina Hurricanes, NHL)

HEADLESS HORSEMAN (Sleepy Hollow High, New York)

HITMEN (Stuyvesant High, New York, baseball)

THUNDER CHICKEN (Stuart High, New York)

Ballhogs

If you play basketball you've probably been on teams that should have been called the Ballhogs. These are the players who want all the glory (and all the points) and never pass the ball. They just won't pass! Heck, a ballhog wouldn't pass you the orange juice at breakfast. What you may not know is that ballhogs also never pee. To do that, they'd have to pass water, and ballhogs never pass! (Interesting fact: Girls are rarely ballhogs.)

So how should you deal with these loons? Truthfully, I have no idea. But next time I'm stuck with a ballhog on my basketball team, I'm going to hire Stormy the Ice Hog to put a hurtin' on him.

Olympic Mischief

As you know, the Olympic Games are held every four years to find out who are the best athletes in the world. Mighty warriors in badminton, ping-pong, and rhythmic gymnastics go out to test their strength, speed, and good, old-fashioned

Fun Basketball Lingo!

Hospital pass: Making a pass that is so weak, you may as well have thrown it from a hospital bed.

Tug of Wussies

Tug-of-war was an Olympic sport until 1920. It was cancelled partially because there had been a huge controversy between the U.S. and British teams at earlier games. The Americans accused the Brits of cheating because they wore spiked cleats. (That could have been dangerous. Double-crossing your tug-of-war opponent can result in a knot that takes hours to untangle.)

guts against each other on the field of competition. Heck, even a bare-bones Olympic event like skeleton[7] draws dozens of howling spectators.

But can average people like you and me (well, maybe just you) also take part in Olympic Games? *Yes!* For our role model, we should look at the Office Olympics. (Yes, these are real.) In the O.O. (ooh!) flabby businesspeople compete in events like the wastebasket toss. (This complex

---

7. Look it up!

game involves trying to shoot paper balls into a wastebasket.) Other competitions include paper-clip-chain making and rubber-band shooting (tips on marksmanship at the end of this chapter).

All of this build-up should have you anxious to form an Olympic committee to host your own version of the Olympics. If you need a couple of ideas to get started, try:

ALL NIGHT LONG: Contestants position themselves comfortably and attempt to stay up all night long. Some will not make it. A digital camera should be on hand so that the winner can have evidence of victory. Drug testers will ensure that no coffee, tea, Mountain Dew, or methamphetamines are consumed. Extra credit for telling boring stories about your family that will make your opponents go into a mini-coma. (Caution: These stories may make *you* go into a mini-coma.)

DISQUALIFICATION FOR "RESTING THE EYES."

STUPID NINJA MOVES: This competition works best with four or more players. Each competitor gives him- or herself a trademarked Stupid Ninja Move. While this should remotely resemble a martial-arts attack, it can be invented and should, in some way, be stupid. Players must make either an appropriate sound effect while making their move OR shout out a word or phrase to accompany it (i.e., "Jaguar Kick!" "Won Tons SUCK!" or "Super Sissy Chop!")

The players stand and each gives his or her Stupid Ninja Move and sound. Play then starts in reverse alphabetical order by middle name. The first player makes his or her Stupid Ninja Move and follows it with another player's move. The player who was imitated makes his or her own move, followed by another player's. (It can't be the player who just called them out, though.) *THIS MUST HAPPEN QUICKLY*.

As play progresses, a player is eliminated for making the wrong Ninja Move, giving the wrong sound or phrase for the move, going out of turn, or going too slow.

If it gets down to two people who can quickly and flawlessly imitate each other back and forth, it is a tie. The two players must then fight to the death.

DISQUALIFICATION FOR ANYONE WHO (A) KNOWS MARTIAL ARTS OR (B) ACTUALLY LOOKS SORT OF COOL WHEN DOING HIS OR HER STUPID NINJA MOVES.

The Paralympics are held the same year as the Olympics. They feature athletes from different disability groups, including athletes with mental disabilities. In 2000, Spain's basketball team crushed its competition at the Paralympics held in Sydney, Australia. They easily beat every opponent and won the gold medal. But their gold medal was revoked when it was revealed that ten of the team's players were *faking* their mental disability. They were actually people with "normal" brain functions!

Although these muttonheads were caught, this raises an interesting question: How mentally disabled is a non-mentally disabled person who tries to win a gold medal for the mentally disabled? With these thoughts, we now turn to . . .

The Best Sports Underwear Story of All Time!

Maybe odd things always happen in Sydney. Take Barry Larkin, for instance. He lived in Sydney in 1956, the year that Australia hosted the Summer Olympics. As usual, before the games started, the Olympic torch was lit and then carried cross-country by various runners to the games' location.

When the Olympic flame came to Sydney, the idea was that a runner would present the Olympic torch to the mayor of Sydney. The mayor would make a speech and then give the torch to the next runner in line. So on the day of the big event, hordes of people came out to witness the passing of the torch. Photographers snapped pictures and the crowd went wild as the runner passed them by, flaming torch held high. With a police escort, the runner leaped toward the mayor and handed him the torch.

It took the mayor a moment to notice the torch was a chair leg painted silver, with a can stuck to the top. Inside the can was a pair of flaming underwear, burning with a nasty flame. It was a practical joke! This guy was an Olympic underwear torch poser!

By the time people figured out that the hoaxer had "jockeyed" into position in front of the "real" torch-bearer, he was long gone. And while Barry Larkin was later identified as the underwear trickster, he managed to avoid punishment. In fact, to some people, he was sort of an underground (underwear?) hero![8]

---

8. Hey, I wonder if the Flaming Underwears would make a good mascot?

The Point of the Story: It can be fun to set your underwear on fire.

The Pointier Point of the Story: After committing mischief, leave the scene quickly.

Gravity Attack!

I'm guessing the odds are pretty good that you and your friends are daredevils. And as you skateboard, do bike stunts, and bungee jump from orbiting satellites, there will be times when someone (hopefully your Nemesis!) has a brutal wipeout. This will give you the opportunity to use one of the following choice words:

BACON STRIPS: No, not a reference to dirty underwear. This describes the long scabs of road rash someone gets from wiping out on asphalt.

BEEF: Landing on your butt.

BIFF: To wipe out.

192

CHUNDER: Another good word for biffing.

CLOON: Smashing into the ground and not getting up again very fast.

CORE SAMPLE: Bike handlebars are made of hollow tubing. If someone wipes out and lands on the end of their handlebar, it can act like a cookie cutter . . . and there you have a core sample.

CORN DOG: To wipe out and get all covered in dirt.[9]

CRAYON MARK: The blood and snot left behind on the road after a good chunder.

ENDO: Wiping out on a bike and flipping end-over-end over the handlebars.

FACE-PLANT: Not a parsnip growing from your nostril! This is when you land on your face during a wipeout.

---

9. National Corn Dog Day is March 17. The corn dog's inventor, Ed Waldmire Jr., originally wanted to call it the Crunchy Cur.

FDGB: An abbreviation for the brilliant statement, "Fall Down, Go Boom."

GRAVITY ATTACK: I think you get the idea.

HANG UP: When the front or back of a skateboard gets caught on something and the rider has an involuntary dismount.

IDIOTMOBILE: The kind of car that bad drivers seem to own.

INVOLUNTARY DISMOUNT: A crash.

LETHAL PROJECTILE: Someone who's out of control and will soon chunder or corn dog.

MANZONE: The region of a male's body that he really doesn't want hurt. "Why has Jimmy been lying on the ground for an hour?" "His handlebar hit him in the manzone."

MUNCHIE: A cut, scrape, bruise, or contusion from wiping out.

RENTAL RODENT: A kid on a rented snowboard or skis.

SUCK MILK: When a surfer or water-skier wipes out, they drink white water, or "suck milk."

WORKED: To have the snow, sea, ground, or road really crush you. You can also be drilled or nailed.

YARD SALE: A wipeout so serious that the person is sprawled on the ground with all their equipment spread around them.

If you have a friend who suffers from a face-plant or a munchie, you can help.

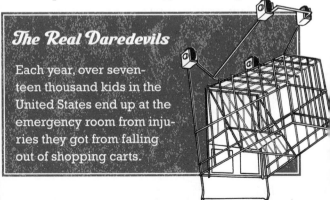

The Real Daredevils

Each year, over seventeen thousand kids in the United States end up at the emergency room from injuries they got from falling out of shopping carts.

According to R. U. O'Kaye's book *Helping the Chundered*, you should be sympathetic! Here are some things you can say that will help your friend feel better.

"I am here for you."

"What hurts you hurts me."

"I'll tell your mother that you love her."

"Turn that frown upside down! Oh wait, you already are upside down."

"It's okay if you cry. I won't tell."

As a result of a gravity attack, you may get the opportunity to sign someone's cast. Sweet! This is a chance to show off how clever you are!

If it's a broken arm:
"Next time, break a leg!"

Broken anything:
"Milk: It does a body good."

Rubber Bands!

Learning how to shoot rubber bands is important to your career as a mischief maker.

BUT BEFORE WE START, YOU HAVE TO READ THESE TWO WORDS: *EYE PROTECTION!*

I have seen firsthand the damage that a rubber band can do to the eye. It's horrible! So if you already wear glasses, keep wearing them. If not, put on some protective goggles. If you have a paintball helmet, put that over the top of all of it. And make sure that anyone else in the vicinity has the same protection!

Speaking of protection, you have probably already discovered that the heavier your rubber band, the more distance and accuracy you get, but also the more pain! Rubber band expert Tim Morgan suggests a number 31 band; these are available at office supply shops . . . and hunting stores.

Common Mistakes

Don't pull the rubber band back too far! It may break (ouch) or backfire (double ouch.) In rare instances, pulling too far on a rubber band may also lead to spontaneous human combustion.[10]

Grips

PREHISTORIC GRIP

This is the grip that Neanderthal rubber band hunters used when going after game like the woolly mammoth and the

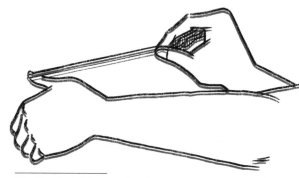

---

10. Aka "catching on fire."

cave hamster. While this is an easy way to shoot a rubber band, your aim and velocity won't be very good.

For a much more accurate method using this style, hook the rubber band around the end of a pen.

MEDIEVAL GRIP

In medieval times, inventions like the crossbow and the loofah changed the way that rubber bands were fired. The Medieval Grip was developed by a monk who used it to keep wolves away from his radishes.

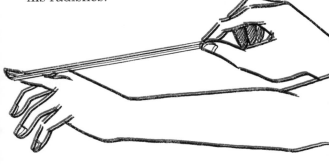

To use it, loop the rubber band around the middle finger of your left hand. (If you're left-handed, loop around your right hand and reverse these directions.) Now pinch the other end of the rubber band with your other hand. Raise and extend your left arm and pull back with your right hand. Sight and fire!

TWENTY-FIRST-CENTURY GRIP

In the modern age, this is the preferred way to shoot rubber bands. It looks cool, it's more accurate, and it only takes one hand to fire. (Translation: You can be sneakier with it.) It does take a little practice to learn the setup, though.

1. *LOOP ONE END OF THE RUBBER BAND AROUND THE END OF YOUR LITTLE FINGER.*

2. *PUT YOUR HAND IN THE SAME SHAPE AS IN THE DIAGRAM. (PRETEND YOU'RE A COWBOY.)*

3. *WITH YOUR NONSHOOTING HAND, PULL THE RUBBER BAND UP AND AROUND THE BASE OF YOUR THUMB.*

4. *STRETCH THE RUBBER BAND COMPLETELY AROUND THE END OF YOUR INDEX (POINTING) FINGER.*

5. *AIM YOUR FINGER AT A TARGET. WHEN YOU'RE READY TO SHOOT, JUST RELEASE THE END YOU'RE HOLDING WITH YOUR PINKIE.*

With a little practice, you'll be a regular rubber band deadeye! (But you still need to wear deadeye protection, right?)

Note: Once you have practiced and mastered this grip, you can load additional rubber bands on your other fingers as well, for a total of three bands on one hand. This makes reloading a snap!

Fake Finch Fouls Fans

George Plimpton wrote an article for *Sports Illustrated* in 1985 that described an amazing baseball player from Nepal named Sidd Finch. Using yoga and ancient mind–body techniques, Finch could supposedly throw a fastball at 168 miles an hour. (Most big-league pitchers have fastballs in the 90s.)

Plimpton's article told how the New York Mets were giving the new pitcher a tryout. Finch pitched with one foot bare and one in a hiking boot. When he threw the ball, it went so fast that nobody could see it. The baseball would leave his hand and then just reappear in the catcher's glove. Mets fans went nuts, and thousands of readers believed the story. They shouldn't have; the first letter of each word at the story's beginning gave it away: "He's a pitcher, part yogi and part recluse. Impressively liberated from our opulent life-style, Sidd's deciding about yoga."[11]

11. "H-a-p-p-y A-p-r-i-l F-o-o-l-s D-a-y."

Duels

"*I THOROUGHLY DISAPPROVE OF DUELS. IF A MAN SHOULD CHALLENGE ME, I WOULD TAKE HIM KINDLY AND FORGIVINGLY BY THE HAND AND LEAD HIM TO A QUIET PLACE AND KILL HIM.*"
—*Mark Twain*

Back in the day, if a mischief maker offended the wrong person, he or she might be challenged to a duel. Although duels usually involved guns or swords, they were not always fought to the death. Other types of weapons could be used; duelists have used harpoons and even water balloons.

A duel is initiated when a person feels that he or she has been insulted by another. Here are a couple of relatively safe duels that you and your Nemesis can share together:

Insult Duel

The key to a good Insult Duel is to have impartial judges on hand who can decide a winner. There also has to be a limit to an Insult Duel, or it will go on forever and turn into a mere Cut-Down Contest. To avoid this, each duelist gets three chances to land his or her best shot. Afterwards, the judges pick the person with the most venomous tongue. (Tips on good insults can be found on page 138.)

Rubber Band Chess Duel

In a "real" duel, the two combatants usually had close friends on hand to act as assistants. Called "seconds," these friends were in charge of weapons and helping to ensure that no cheating took place. You will need to have a trusted second for the Rubber Band Chess Duel. To engage, you will need a couple of high-quality rubber bands and two bandannas. The duel can take place in a large room or outdoors, and it will end when one duelist (the winner) hits the other duelist (the loser) first with a rubber band. Have an impartial judge on hand to decide what a "hit" is.

Each duelist loads his or her pockets with rubber bands. The seconds each take a bandanna and carefully wrap it around the head of the enemy duelist. It is the second's responsibility to ensure that the duelist cannot see *anything*.

The seconds lead their trusted duelists to a spot that is far enough away from the other that a launched rubber band could not travel the distance. (See page 200 for tips on firing.)

Once it is clear that each duelist is blind, silence begins. The *only* people who are allowed to speak are the seconds. (If one of the duelists is unable to follow this rule, he or she loses immediately.)

The seconds now serve as coaches. Each duelist gets a turn, with the duelist whose last name is longer going first. The second will instruct the duelist to take ONE of the following: (1) two steps or (2) one step and a shot or (3) two shots from a stationary position. The instructions might sound like this:

"Take two steps straight forward and lie on the ground." (This presents a more difficult target to hit.)

"Take one step left and fire your rubber band straight ahead."

"Aim a rubber band shot ahead and to your left. You missed! This time shoot a little more downward."

As soon as one of the duelists scores a hit on the other, the duel is over. The winner gets bragging rights and the loser must quietly slink away.

Note: This duel also works with water balloons. The bandannas serve as eye protection. If you're using cheap bandannas, use two, or put safety glasses over them. (Pants and long-sleeved shirts optional.)

There have been some pretty weird dueling stories over the years. For example, in 1813, two Frenchmen fought a duel (to the death!) using broom handles. The winner had to clean up the mess.

THIRTY YEARS LATER TWO DIFFERENT FRENCHMEN FOUGHT A DUEL (TO THE DEATH!) BY THROWING BILLIARD BALLS AT EACH OTHER. (THERE'S NOTHING WORSE THAN ASKING THE MAGIC 8-BALL A QUESTION WHEN IT'S COMING AT YOU AT EIGHTY MILES AN HOUR.)

And in 1894, two British men in India dueled (to the death!) by going into a dark room with a cobra in it. Whoever left first was chicken. A little later, one man was dead and one was a live chicken.

Americans once used another unique weapon for dueling: shoes. In early America, duelists would put on shoes with copper toes, grab each other by the collar, and start kicking each other in the ankles. (This process was called "purring.") The duel ended when one of the two people gave up. The winner could then shout something like "I kicked the shins out of you!" or "I kicked your ankles!"

An odd type of duel that was popular in Turkey was forehead dueling. The two adversaries couldn't use their hands or feet. Instead, they would rush at each other like billy goats and smash their heads together. As usual, whoever gave up first lost, and was known as a "butt head loser" for the rest of his life.

But the finest dueling story of all time concerns a president of the United States. (No, not Andrew Jackson, although he did kill a man in a duel because he said something mean to Jackson's wife.) In 1842, before he became president, Abraham Lincoln wrote a number of unsigned letters to a newspaper that mocked a politician named James Shields. Mr. Shields somehow found out that Lincoln was responsible for these letters and challenged Lincoln to a duel. Luckily for our country, the rule was that the challenged person got to pick the weapons for the duel. And in his wisdom, Abraham Lincoln chose cow manure. Dueling dookie! Yes, the two men would fight to the death throwing cow pies at each other.

LINCOLN WAS OBVIOUSLY MAKING FUN OF DUELS, AND HIS KOOKY SUGGESTION JUST MADE SHIELDS ANGRIER.

Eventually, Lincoln agreed to a duel with swords, but he insisted that they

209

be the biggest, heaviest swords that were made. (James Shields was a short man.) The two men did nearly duel, but once everyone saw how gigantic the swords were, the duel was called off on the grounds that it was very silly.

Bodily Mischief

You will need a good education to become a wise guy or smarty girl. (I just made that up: *smarty girl.* It could be the cool new slang!) But unluckily for you, there is no way that one book (even one as awesome as this) can contain all the information you are going to need to know. For that, you're going to have to pay attention in class for years.

I know, it's tragic.

BUT AT LEAST BY THE TIME YOU'RE DONE WITH THIS CHAPTER, YOU WILL BE SUPERIOR TO ALL THE PUNK "KNOW-IT-ALLS" AND NAMBY-PAMBY "HONOR STUDENTS" ON YOUR STREET.

Don't hold that against them, though. It's not that know-it-alls are so bad; it's just that they don't know the right kinds of information. Sure, they'll happily tell you many details about things like concrete, shoelaces, collecting bottle caps, and sword fighting. But who cares about that stuff? Bor-ring!

Know-it-alls need to understand that successful mischief makers (like you!) want information about disgusting things. And once you have that knowledge, you can start sharing it with everyone you know. This will disgust and repel some people (excellent!), but it will also attract just the right element: the future members of your Fan Club (see p. 75). One good person to start sharing your newfound wisdom with is your dad. In fact, he may be so impressed with what you have learned that he will raise your allowance. For example, let your dad know the following:

★ THE AVERAGE MAN SPENDS TEN MINUTES IN THE BATHROOM WHEN HE HAS TO TAKE CARE OF **SERIOUS** BUSINESS.

★ THE AVERAGE MAN HAS 1/10 OF A GRAM OF POOP STREAKS IN HIS UNDERWEAR.[1]

★ THE AVERAGE MAN DOESN'T KNOW WHERE THE MOST DISGUSTING PLACE IN THE HOUSE IS. IT TURNS OUT THAT THE REFRIGERATOR DOOR HANDLE ALMOST ALWAYS HAS MORE GERMS ON IT—INCLUDING POOP GERMS!—THAN ANY OTHER PLACE IN THE HOUSE. TELEPHONES, REMOTE CONTROLS, AND COMPUTER KEYBOARDS ARE ALSO PRETTY BAD.[2]

---

1. Aka "bacon strips" or "fecal material."
2. Believe it or not, the toilet seat in most homes is much cleaner than these other spots. That's because people clean the toilet more than they clean keyboards.

But how do poop molecules get in the kitchen in the first place? Is there a Poop Molecule Fairy who sprinkles disgusting magic dust throughout the house? While that's an interesting theory, it turns out that there are special germs called *fecal coliform* that are found in poop. When you flush the toilet, these little germs become airborne, and they land on nearby things (like your toothbrush) and far away things (like the refrigerator door handle). As Mythbuster Jamie Hyneman says, "Poop is everywhere."

And when Hyneman says "everywhere," he means everywhere. For example, in the northern part of Spain is a place

Quick Mischief

★ Spread Icy Hot or honey on the toilet seat.
★ Unscrew the showerhead and put in food-coloring tablets or bouillon cubes.
★ Put an empty banana peel in someone's pocket.

IBM

If you know someone who has accidentally pooped his pants, help him feel better by telling him he suffers from "involuntary bowel motility." (And if you know someone who poops his pants on purpose, you might be better off not knowing him.)

called Catalonia. A common sight in Catalonia is a statue of someone squatting with their rear end exposed and taking a poop!

These pooping statues have been around since the 1600s. They show *El Caganer*, meaning "the great pooper." In this part of the world, symbols of poop and of people pooping are associated with good health. For example, the people of Catalan sometimes say, *"Menjar bé, i caga fort, i no tinguess por de la mort!"* before meals.[3]

---

3. "Eat well, poop strong, and you will have no fear of death!"

The *El Caganer* symbols are especially popular (or poopular) at Christmas, when shops sell pastries shaped like poop logs. And on Christmas Eve, kids beat on a hollow log named "*Caga tió*" (poop log) that is packed with gifts. Then the kids all sing a song to get the log to poop its gifts out the end. It's sort of a pooping piñata!

Here is one of the songs the children sing to the log. Please sing this aloud now:

Caga tió	Poop log
tió de Nadal	log of Christmas
no caguis arengades	don't poop salty fish
que són salads.	which are not good.
Caga torrons	Poop almond candies
que son mes bons!	which are much better!

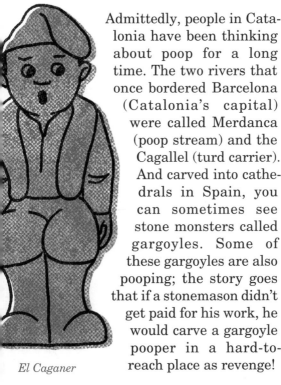

El Caganer

Admittedly, people in Catalonia have been thinking about poop for a long time. The two rivers that once bordered Barcelona (Catalonia's capital) were called Merdanca (poop stream) and the Cagallel (turd carrier). And carved into cathedrals in Spain, you can sometimes see stone monsters called gargoyles. Some of these gargoyles are also pooping; the story goes that if a stonemason didn't get paid for his work, he would carve a gargoyle pooper in a hard-to-reach place as revenge!

When Spaniards began colonizing North America, they came into contact with Native Americans for the first time. Members of the Navajo tribe found their overseas visitors strange in many ways. Because of their "bizarre" behavior, the Navajo thought that the Spaniards didn't have poop chutes (aka anuses). I guess someone should have told them about *El Caganer!*

If you're ever stuck for a good gift for your dad, a company has begun selling something called the Underwear Safe. It is a safe disguised as dirty underwear. The men's briefs have a secret compartment inside, but to get to it, a thief would have to go past the underwear's realistic-looking skid marks on the lower rear

Caga Tió Slang

★ Voodoo butter: A way to describe the *caga tió* in English.
★ Prairie dog: A *caga tió* that comes out a little bit, and then retreats back inside you.
★ "Dropping the Browns off at the Super Bowl": An expression describing a trip to the bathroom.

portion. One size fits all! The Underwear Safe comes in white (and brown).[4]

What's the difference between an oral and a rectal thermometer?[5]

At this point, some of you may be getting sort of grossed out, but don't be. Pooping is only natural. After all, there was a lot of pooping on the day you were born. You see, when women have babies, they almost always "void their bowels." (That's fancy talk for taking a poop.) So don't act like it doesn't have anything to do with you. It always has, ever since Day One!

What's the worst thing that can happen to a sleeping bat?[6]

But pooping can be dangerous. A male

4. In Japan, you can buy underwear from vending machines. (You can also buy rice, fresh flowers, and live lobsters!)
5. The taste.
6. Diarrhea.

What a Crappy Book!

When this book was being put together, I was hoping that it could be printed on elephant poop. You see, elephants eat a lot of fiber, and they only digest 45 percent of it. That means that their poop can be used for paper!

The Elephant Dung Paper company boils elephant poop for five hours. Then they bleach, spin, color, spread, and dry the poop, and *voilà*! Elephant dung paper! Those elephants can really keep you turning the pages, too. The average elephant poops enough poop to make 115 pages a day. And there are also companies making paper from panda bear poop and sheep poop.

So how can you get in on this action? The first step involves eating a *lot* of fiber. I recommend bran flakes, asparagus, and a sprinkling of sawdust on every meal. Then follow the simple steps outlined above to make your own poop paper. Use it to make paper for school and work assignments. And nothing says "I care" as much as a birthday card you made yourself! (It's not that hard; in fact, that's how I produced all the paper that this book was printed on. I was able to make 65 pages a day!)

hippo can fire strong jets of poop and pee out its rear end when it's claiming territory. And even more frightening is what happened in the English town of Hanley. City officials there installed a custom public toilet called a "superloo." It was a great place for downtown visitors to take a break . . . or at least it was until the superloo exploded!

Apparently, high voltage cables running under the toilet had a power surge, and the superloo blew its roof off, leaving smoke pouring out of it. A spokesperson said that the explosion "could have been quite distressing . . . if someone had been in there." Distressing? How about terrifying? I don't think I'd ever be able to "skip to my loo" again!

The only thing more frightening than having a toilet blow up beneath you would be having a ninja assassin hiding in the toilet and waiting for you to make an appearance. In 1578, a Japanese warlord named Uesugi Kenshin was busting a grumpy when this happened to him. Apparently, the ninja had been camped out in the cesspit for days, waiting for just the right butt to appear above him. And when it did, the ninja sliced and diced. (This kind of gives "Look out below!" a whole new meaning, huh?)

As dangerous as bowel movements can be, passing gas can be equally lethal. Perhaps you have seen the famous tombstone that reads: "Wherever you be, let the wind blow free, for holding it in was the death of me." If you are "bottled up" and need to relieve some pressure, you have two choices.

1. IIF YOU ARE NEAR YOUR NEMESIS (LET'S SAY, WITHIN A MILE), LET YOUR WIND BLOW FREE. THAT WAY HE CAN APPRECIATE YOUR INNER BEAUTY.

2. OTHERWISE, YOU SHOULD DISCREETLY WALK A LITTLE WAY AWAY FROM WHOMEVER YOU'RE AROUND BEFORE PLAYING THE BUTT BONGOS. IF SOMEONE ASKS YOU WHY YOU ARE WANDERING OFF, JUST USE THE MOTTO OF THE COAST GUARD'S RESCUE SWIMMERS: "SO THAT OTHERS MAY LIVE."

Leave No Seat Unturned

Make it a habit to visit the bathroom when you visit someone else's house. You know what I mean? Even if the house is a nice house, *really* go to the bathroom.

The Apple o' Death!

Let's take a break from this scatological material[7] for this charming activity.

HALLOWEEN IS THE MOST OBVIOUS TIME TO PLAY THIS DEADLY AND EFFECTIVE JOKE, BUT IT COULD WORK AT ANY TIME OF THE YEAR.

You see, there have been lots of urban legends about evil people putting razor blades into apples for trick-or-treaters. Although these stories are almost always myths, everyone knows them. Use this to your advantage! All you need is an apple (surprise) and some red food dye or a ketchup packet (double surprise).

Secretly take your red food-dye packet, tear the corner slightly, and "squirrel" it away inside your mouth. Picking up your apple, go into the kitchen or wherever your "victim" might be. Hold up the apple proudly and say something about

_____
7. Look it up. (Then use it as much as possible.)

how the nice but slightly strange lady down the street gave it to you.

Then bite into it. Look shocked, and if you're a good actor, scream. Let the red food dye escape from your mouth while yelling something incoherent about "razor blades." Oh, the fun you'll have!

AND NOW THE TIME HAS COME TO TALK ABOUT WORMS. NOT EARTHWORMS, WHICH LIVE IN THE DIRT, BUT TAPEWORMS.

Hint: They don't live in tape. Too sticky! Nope, tapeworms live in your guts. These worms can set up shop deep inside your intestines, and although they start off pretty small, they can get awfully big. You wouldn't believe me if I told you how big.

Wrong Place, Right Time

A friend of mine once went into a clothing store's changing room and then called out, "Hey, there's no toilet paper in here!"

225

Your intestines wind around and around inside your body, sort of like a coil of hose or rope. And as the tapeworm gets longer, it also coils around inside you. So, here goes: a woman in Mississippi supposedly had a tapeworm that was thirty-seven feet long inside of her. There have been other documented cases of twenty- to-thirty-foot-long tapeworms inside humans. That's not a worm, it's a poop python!

Where do these worms come from? If you eat meat that is raw or semi-raw, it may contain the eggs or larvae of one of the three species of tapeworm . . . yep, you have your choice of three flavors: there's the pork tapeworm, the fish tapeworm, and the beef tapeworm. (Collect them all!) Even if you get just one of these worms, some of them can lay a million eggs a day, so you'll be getting more whether you want them or not.

Good News
It is easy to cure a tapeworm attack. Modern medicine works miracles.

Bad News

Some tapeworms will eventually work their way out of your body. We can't tell you how. It's too horrible.

Luckily, there are other disgusting things we can talk about, too. For example, there is sweat, pee, blood, and bacteria (which is what makes things stink). A recent study found that the public areas with the highest concentration of these substances were playgrounds and day care centers. Public restrooms were only half as gross as the top two, ranking about the same as escalator handrails, shopping cart handles, and vending machine buttons. (What's going on? Is there some stinky person out there who is sweating, peeing, bleeding, and using a lot of vending machines?)

Do you know what the smelliest

> ### *News Flash!*
>
> According to recent research, the sweatiest city in the United States is Phoenix, Arizona. Congratulations!

animal in the world is?[8] It is the African zorilla. This isn't a gorilla with a BO problem; the zorilla actually looks like a skunk, but it smells even worse. A famous zoologist said that it has the most "well-developed anal glands in the animal kingdom." Sweet! Zorillas stink so badly, they don't even hang out with each other. And yet, amazingly, one tribe of East Africans uses the scent of the zorilla as perfume. Beauty is in the nose of the beholder. (And so is your finger. Do you mind?)

HERE'S ONE OF THE WORST STORIES I'VE HEARD IN A WHILE. WAY BACK IN THE TWENTIETH CENTURY, A MAN WHO LIVED IN MISSISSIPPI OPENED UP HIS CHEWING TOBACCO AND STUFFED SOME LEAF IN HIS MOUTH. HE NOTICED SOMETHING IN THE TOBACCO THAT DIDN'T BELONG THERE. HE SPIT THE ITEM OUT. IT WAS A HUMAN TOE.

In a weird coincidence, the man who found the toe got *ptomaine* (toe-main!)

---

8. Stop looking at me!

poisoning from this horrible experience. And that is why nobody should chew tobacco, even though it is fun to spit tobacco juice. By the way, a camel can spit over twenty feet if it gets upset. (Lesson: Don't mess with camels.) But camels don't spit spit. Instead, they spit stomach juice and whatever else might be in their tummy. Nice!

Believe it or not, I drive around with a spitting camel in my backseat. Okay, it's not really a camel, it's a dog named Dizzy. And Dizzy doesn't really spit, she just drools long gobbets of saliva. Then she shakes her head and the strands of spit go flying onto my head and into my ears. It's horrible. (I need a new camel!)

A Dog By Any Other Name

Dogs that are a cross of two breeds often get interesting names. For example, the crossbreed of a shih tzu and a bulldog is called a bullshih.

Well, as I've been writing this charming chapter, I've been trying to think of the most horrible thing I can imagine. Hey, I think I did it! The chapter must now end.[9]

Gravy Boat Float

When it comes to soft drinks, many people stick to just a couple of flavors. And some folks even make a big deal about how nearly identical brands (like Coke and Pepsi) are really quite different. Muttonheads!

For these misguided souls, buy some turkey-and-gravy-flavored pop. Jones Soda bottles this wonderful stuff every November. Tell your victim that they have to try the latest, greatest soda. Pour a glass for you and your mark (so that he doesn't get suspicious). Trust me, there is no better Thanksgiving surprise than to see a soft drink snob grimacing in agony and exclaiming, "Tastes like . . . gravy!"

9. Imagine Siamese twins connected at the mouth. One of them is throwing up.

Lessons FROM Stravinsky

Someone has probably complained about you by now. But don't feel bad; these people are just jealous. After all, you have a copy of this book and they don't! There's another reason you shouldn't be discouraged by someone else's complaints. After reading this chapter, you'll be able to complain better than anyone.

The key to proper complaining is to do it

in an unexpected, creative, or funny way. There are some people who are so good at making these kinds of complaints, they should have black belts in it. For example, it's possible that throughout history, no group has had as much to complain about as the Jewish people. They even have a word for their style of

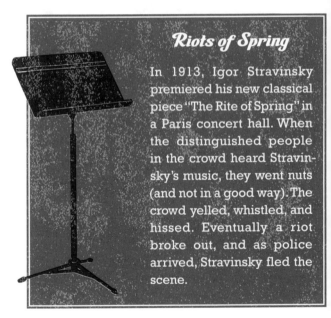

Riots of Spring

In 1913, Igor Stravinsky premiered his new classical piece "The Rite of Spring" in a Paris concert hall. When the distinguished people in the crowd heard Stravinsky's music, they went nuts (and not in a good way). The crowd yelled, whistled, and hissed. Eventually a riot broke out, and as police arrived, Stravinsky fled the scene.

complaining: *kvetching* (ka-vetch-ing).

The beauty of good kvetching is that you don't have to complain about something that's bothering you right now. For example, at the moment you are perfectly happy reading this book. Now imagine that your sister has wandered into the room with you.

YOUR SISTER (ENVIOUSLY): I'VE HEARD THAT THE BOOK YOU'RE READING IS PRETTY AWESOME.

YOU (THINKING BACK TO EARLIER UNHAPPY MEMORIES): YEAH, BUT I'VE READ SO MANY BAD BOOKS IN MY TIME, IT'S ABOUT TIME ONE OF THEM WAS ANY GOOD!

See what you did there? You complained even though you were happy! This is the secret to excellent kvetching. Anyone can complain about something bad that is happening in the present. But it takes special talent to complain about the past!

Kvetching in a crowd can also be rewarding—you know, like at a basketball game when your team isn't trying very hard? (Or maybe at your brother's recital when he *is* trying.) Depending on the situation, sometimes the best way to release your frustration is to boo.

BOOING IS NOT NECESSARILY BAD; IT'S JUST A WAY TO EXPRESS YOUR OPINION OR FEELINGS ABOUT WHAT YOU SEE.

Now, some people will tell you that booing is always impolite and barbaric. But is that true? Opera is a form of entertainment enjoyed by some of the most educated and polite people on the planet. And opera fans dressed in their gowns and tuxedoes have been known to boo an opera singer right off the stage if he or she doesn't deliver the goods.

The idea of booing a performance dates back at least to the early 1800s, when people apparently imitated the sound of a cow mooing to express their displeasure.

And today, in places like the British House of Commons, politicians energetically cheer and boo each other's speeches. By the way, most people are generally more positive than negative when they're in crowds. Researchers have found that on average, applause lasts for eight seconds, but booing rarely lasts for even three.

NOT EVERYBODY IN THE WORLD BOOS. AS ANYBODY WHO'S EVER SEEN A SOCCER MATCH OUTSIDE THE UNITED STATES CAN TELL YOU, WHISTLING IS PROBABLY THE MOST COMMON WAY TO "BOO."

Hissing is also popular, and this practice is as old as the ancient Romans, who would hiss a performer if they didn't like him until he retreated in disgrace.

You have to use good judgment when deciding how and when to kvetch or boo at a sporting event or performance. The smaller and quieter the crowd, the more polite you should be. That means that if you're at a game where the players and referees can actually hear you, you shouldn't be yelling at them. But if you're in a bigger crowd where it's unlikely they could hear you, enjoy yourself!

All~Star Booing: Philadelphia

No group has become more famous for booing than the fans in Philadelphia. Of course, you could say that they have good reason to boo. After all, in 2007, the Philadelphia Phillies lost their ten thousandth game, which is a record for any sports franchise. So these sad and disappointed Philadelphia fans will boo anybody. Some of their lowlights:

Quick Mischief

★ Buy the smallest heart-shaped picture frame you can find. Then put a picture of yourself in the frame. The next time you visit friends or family, slip the picture onto their hearth, desk, or bookshelf. If you don't make the picture too obvious, it may be months (or even years!) before they discover it.

At halftime in an Eagles football game, a band started playing the song "Here Comes Santa Claus." As a man dressed as Santa ran downfield, a wave of boos from over fifty thousand fans snowed down on him. By the time Santa got to the end zone, the boos were followed by snowballs. Philadelphia has been known as "the city that booed Santa" ever since.

POSSIBLE EXCUSE: People in Philadelphia don't like Christmas.

Matthew Scott was one of the first people in the world to get a hand transplant. Using his new hand, Matthew threw out the first pitch at a Philadelphia Phillies baseball game. But when Scott's throw fell short of home plate, the boos rained down.

POSSIBLE EXCUSE: The fans were booing Scott's surgeon.

Kobe Bryant is from Philadelphia. But when the NBA All-Star Game was played there, the fans booed Kobe Bryant every time he touched the ball. And when Kobe won the game's MVP trophy, he got booed even more, and chants of "Kobe sucks" began.

POSSIBLE EXCUSE 1: Philadelphia fans don't like anyone. (After all, the same crowd booed Beyoncé during the game's halftime show.)

POSSIBLE EXCUSE 2: Kobe sucks.

> In 2006, the Cincinnati Bengals set up a hotline at 381-JERK where people could report fans who were being obnoxious.

Be True TO YOUR School

"O MISCHIEF, THOU ART SWIFT TO ENTER IN THE THOUGHTS OF DESPERATE MEN!" —William Shakespeare

You may be surprised to hear this, but you should make sure to have good relationships with your teachers. You know why? A teacher is one of the most powerful beings on the planet. Naturally, a teacher wields her authority in the classroom, but outside of her natural habitat she is even more fearsome. So get on your teacher's good side and you're set for life.

Dumb and Dumbledore

In the 1200s, a man named John Duns Scotus thought that a pointy hat could make a person smarter. The idea was that the point on the cap would help to focus the person's thoughts. John Duns Scotus believed this explained why wizards and witches and other people with secret knowledge wore these kinds of hats.

People who agreed with John Duns Scotus started wearing pointy hats, and were called Dunsmen. However, since it seemed like a silly idea, the pointy "Duns" cap soon became a symbol of stupidity, not intelligence. Eventually, in early American schools, the tradition of keeping a "Dunce" cap for the worst students lasted all the way into the 1950s.

Even more surprising, it turns out teachers actually like kids! (Most kids, anyway.) So although it may sometimes seem like your teachers are out to get you, nothing would make them happier than to see you become a success. (And then to move far, far away.) Best of all, each teacher comes equipped with a sense of humor. This is the only thing that stops them from smacking their heads on the chalkboard when someone says one of the following things for the thousandth time:

"ARE WE DOING ANYTHING IMPORTANT TODAY?"

"I DON'T WANT TO SIT NEXT TO JIMMY. HE SMELLS LIKE HAM."

"I WAS CHEWING MY PENCIL AND ACCIDENTALLY ATE THE ERASER."

"HEY, WHO FARTED? OH, THAT WAS ME."

241

One way to get on your teacher's good side is to be a motivated student. Teachers love having students who want to learn. So on the first day of school, every school year, make a point of telling your teacher that you are a genius. She'll be thrilled to hear it!

YOU: **YOU SHOULD PROBABLY KNOW THAT I'M A GENIUS.**

YOUR TEACHER: **REALLY? HOW DO YOU KNOW THAT?**

YOU: **WELL, I'VE WATCHED ALL OF THE BABY EINSTEIN DVDS.** [1]

Now here is the most surprising advice of all: Turn your assignments in on time and be (somewhat) good in class. Why? Because you can get away with *twice* as many things if you have a good relationship with your teacher than if you don't.

---

1. Note: If you just watched the Baby Einsteins last week, your claim of being a genius will be less convincing.

Take Two Arms and Call Me in the Morning

A boy goes into the hospital for an operation on his legs. When he wakes up after surgery, he yells for the doctor.

"Help, doctor!" he shouts.

"What is it?" asks the doctor, hurrying in.

"I can't feel my legs!" says the boy.

"I know," the doctor answers. *"That's because I cut off your arms."*

This also applies to parents, girlfriends, and boyfriends. In other words, you can bend a lot more rules if you actually follow the rules most of the time. (Repeat that last sentence over and over until you have it memorized.)

Because of your awesome personality and friendly style, others may accuse you of "kissing up" (aka toadying, sucking up,

243

brown nosing, green nostriling) to the teacher. Don't take this too seriously. If you act like it bothers you, then the comments will never end. For one thing, if you really are toadying, it only makes sense that you'd be the teacher's pet!

Anyway, better a butt kisser than a butt wiper: In England during the 1500s, the king had a Groom of the Stool. It was the Groom's job to keep the royal bathroom clean and to wipe the king's butt. You read right: the king was too good to wipe his own butt, so the Groom of the Stool did it for him. (And he also had to lay the king's poop on a plate so that it could be inspected.)

Of course, given your natural instincts, it will be hard to stay out of trouble all the time. For instance, the teacher may ask for your opinion in class. Naturally, this will happen when you're not paying attention. Try saying, "I could not fail to disagree with you less." This means nothing (other than "I agree with you"), but it sounds good and might save the day.

BECAUSE YOU ARE NATURALLY CURIOUS, YOU MIGHT ALSO GET CAUGHT TALKING ABOUT OTHER PEOPLE. A GOOD EXCUSE, ESPECIALLY IN SCIENCE CLASS: "I WASN'T GOSSIPING, MR. ZITZBERGER, I WAS THEORIZING."

But probably the most likely question you'll need to answer is this one: "Why were you late?" While explaining, "I got caught in a sliding, revolving door" has a certain appeal, I recommend trying this one: "Haven't you seen the sign out front? It says 'School Zone Go Slow.'"

Oh, and I have to tell you one of the best excuses that I heard in the classroom: "We didn't copy from each other for the essay. It's just that we've been friends so long, we think alike now!"

Wisdom of the Ages

A girl learns that the wisest person in the world lives on a mountain behind her neighborhood. The girl decides she needs to speak with this person, and she starts hiking up the mountain. It's a long, difficult climb, but finally the girl finds who she's looking for: an old woman with long gray hair staring peacefully off into the distance.

Bowing respectfully, the girl says, *"Oh wise one, I have come to ask you what the secret of life is."*

The wise woman smiles. *"Ah, the secret of life. The secret of life is a duck."*

The girl can't believe it. *"I came all the way up here to hear that the secret of life is a duck?"*

The wise woman shrugs and says, *"Okay, maybe it isn't a duck."*

Still, it is possible that you might actually get into trouble at school. Maybe the teacher said, "You are beginning to try my patience," and you answered with, "To be fair, you should try mine sometime!" Whatever it was, now you're going to need a good explanation for your parents. First, try telling them that famous American writer James Fenimore Cooper (author of *The Last of the Mohicans*) was kicked out of Yale University in 1806. Cooper shoved a rag filled with gunpowder through the keyhole of a friend's room and lit it. (It wasn't his first offense.) Whatever you did should look good by comparison!

Members of student governments sometimes create their own political parties. These parties have included the Dead Beet Party (University of Illinois), the Gumby Party (MIT), and the Silly Party (Northwestern).

OH, AND LET'S NOT FORGET THE CUSTODIANS; THEY ALSO HAVE A SENSE OF HUMOR. DO YOU THINK THAT IT'S AN ACCIDENT THAT JUST WHEN YOU REALLY NEED TO GO TO THE BATHROOM, IT HAS A "CLOSED FOR CLEANING" SIGN OUT FRONT?

One custodian told me that one of his strangest emergencies was a boy who was trapped in his pants. The kid had gone to the bathroom and really *had to go* and couldn't get his pants off! He had apparently put his belt on inside out (so that the buckle was facing in, not out). This proved to be almost impossible to get off. But using a blowtorch and some bolt cutters, they eventually freed the boy from his own pants.[2]

Because teaching can be a hard job, put a little ray of sunshine in your teacher's life on your next field trip. Teachers are on red alert during these days. They want to make sure that nobody gets lost

---

2. That could be a cool book title: Trapped Inside My Pants.

Question: What did the cannibal eat when he was on a diet?

Answer: Children.

or falls into a volcano. And one thing your teacher will be especially worried about is whether he or she has brought along the proper medications for the students who might be allergic to bee stings.

Wait until you are too far from the school to actually turn around and go back. Then make a concerned expression and ask your teacher if he or she has your medication. Especially if you don't take meds, the teacher will get anxious: "What? You have medication?"

Now check your lunch bag and smile reassuringly. "Oh, it's okay, I have them with me. But make sure to remind me to take it at lunch. It's really important."

Pause to give your teacher a moment to

No Standing in These Buses!

A town in Florida named Bithlo hosts the annual Figure 8 School Bus Racing Championship. Retired school buses are raced around a figure 8 track, and where it crosses in the middle is where this race turns into a demolition derby.

get curious about what your meds are for. Then add, "They prevent me from catching on fire." Now your teacher has something to think about on that long, boring bus ride. Good job!

Want to Feel Like a Rebel?

During a lunch break or after school, go into an empty classroom with an accomplice who has a cell phone camera. Chew some gum, take your shoes off, and lean back in your chair. Then put your feet up on a desk and pull on a hood or hat. Start talking on a cell phone or listening to an iPod. Have your picture taken. Now clear out before someone comes!

Later, post the photo somewhere so that millions of people will see it. What a rebel! Feels pretty good, doesn't it?

You have probably heard of cases where troublemakers have hacked into school computer systems to change grades. In 2003, a group of high school students in Salem, New Hampshire, did just that, and if they hadn't been greedy, they wouldn't have gotten caught. But by

Burning Down the House

A high school student in Massapequa, New York, got bad grades on his school papers. Determined to destroy the evidence, he set the papers on fire and threw them out the second-story window of his home. Unfortunately, an ember flew back in, starting a fire that burned the home's entire second floor. Oops!

giving themselves straight A's (in classes where some students had D's), parents got suspicious, and the jig was up.

But that scam was still better than what happened in 2007 at a high school in Berlin. A fourteen-year-old and a fifteen-year-old wearing masks took a briefcase full of report cards from a teacher. ("Just give us the grades and nobody will get hurt!") The two schnitzel-brains were quickly arrested. It turned out that they had been hired by a tenth grader who

Dress for Success

A girl is trying on a sweater in front of a mirror. A salesman is nearby.

Girl: *Do you have this in black? I need it for my brother's funeral.*

Salesman: *I'm so sorry! Is the funeral today?*

Girl: *Oh, he's not dead yet.*

Student~Led Conferences Rock!

Many schools have student-led conferences, meaning that you are in charge of the meeting between your parents and your teachers. While this is an easy thing to dread, try to have a little fun with it. Bring some snacks and act like a big shot. Why not? You're in charge! As a teacher, I always hoped that a student would say, "We'll begin with the agenda in a moment. But first, I'd like to tap dance for you."

If your parents have a good sense of humor, try introducing your mom or dad to your teacher by saying, "Mr. Kaputnik, this is my dad. You should probably know that he drinks." While the two adults sputter and wonder what to make of this, quickly add, "Why just this morning I saw him down two cups of coffee."

After breaking the ice like that, the rest of the conference should be a breeze.

didn't want his parents to learn he had flunked a grade. But I'm guessing that the F's would have been easier to explain than hiring report card robbers.

Bad Book Titles!

As your school librarian knows, each year, authors write books with terrible titles. These writers are either mischief makers or insane . . . or both! And to celebrate their achievements, a contest called the Oddest Book Title of the Year is held. Here are some of the nominees and winners over the years (and, yes, these are all real books):

HOW TO AVOID HUGE SHIPS

THE JOY OF CHICKENS

BOMBPROOF YOUR HORSE

LIVING WITH CRAZY BUTTOCKS

*THE STRAY SHOPPING CARTS OF EASTERN NORTH
   AMERICA: A GUIDE TO FIELD IDENTIFICATION*

CELEBRATING BOXES

REUSING OLD GRAVES

HOW TO [POOP] IN THE WOODS
   (*The actual title doesn't use
   the word "poop"!*)

Lucky Number

A man was walking down the street, right by an apartment building. From inside one of the ground-floor apartments, he heard a child's voice yelling, "13! 13! 13!" The man walked up to one of the apartment windows, but the shades were down and he couldn't see inside. "13! 13! 13!" the voice continued. The man was really curious, and he walked to a window that was slightly open. Peeking in, the man called, "Is everything okay in there?" A finger came out the window and poked him in the eye. Then the child's voice started yelling again: "14! 14! 14!"

Mommy Knows Best

"Mommy, Mommy,
Uncle Kevin is bruised!"
"Stop complaining and eat around it."

★ ★ ★

"Mommy, Mommy,
why are we pushing the car off a cliff?"
"Quiet, or you'll wake your father."

★ ★ ★

"Mommy, Mommy, I miss Daddy!"
"Reload and aim more carefully."

*KNITTING WITH DOG HAIR: BETTER A SWEATER FROM
 A DOG YOU KNOW AND LOVE THAN FROM A SHEEP
 YOU'LL NEVER MEET*

WEEDS IN A CHANGING WORLD

LET'S DISCOVER F WORDS

HIGHLIGHTS IN THE HISTORY OF CONCRETE

*THE BOOK OF MARMALADE:
 ITS ANTECEDENTS, ITS HISTORY AND
 ITS ROLE IN THE WORLD TODAY*

And now, here is my choice for a book
that should have won the contest but was
never even nominated!

*THE COMPLETE IDIOT'S GUIDE TO ENHANCING
 SELF-ESTEEM*

Oh, and one last thing: If you see these
titles on your parents' nightstand, you
might want to try being good for a
change:

NOT-VERY-GIFTED CHILDREN AND YOU

ROLLING PINS, WOODEN SPOONS, AND SPATULAS: KIDS, DISCIPLINE, AND COOKING

ATTEN-TION! THE BEST MILITARY SCHOOLS IN THE NATION

School Buzzword Bingo

Hurray, it's Buzzword Bingo time! As you can see, the Bingo card on the next page has been filled in with words or phrases you probably come across at school. Just cross off items as you notice them, and if you get five in a row, you win! Shout out "Bingo!" and hold up your card. Your teacher will be pleased to see that you were paying attention, and a fabulous prize will be yours.

Of course, every teacher is unique, so feel free to make up your own cards and share them with your friends.

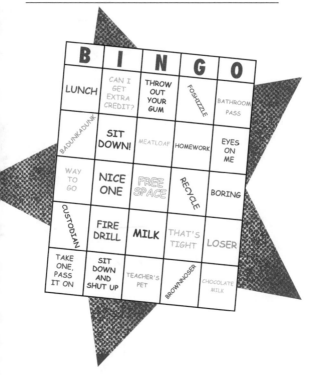

B	I	N	G	O
LUNCH	CAN I GET EXTRA CREDIT?	THROW OUT YOUR GUM	FOSHIZZLE	BATHROOM PASS
BADUNKADUNK	SIT DOWN!	MEATLOAF	HOMEWORK	EYES ON ME
WAY TO GO	NICE ONE	FREE SPACE	RECYCLE	BORING
CUSTODIAN	FIRE DRILL	MILK	THAT'S TIGHT	LOSER
TAKE ONE, PASS IT ON	SIT DOWN AND SHUT UP	TEACHER'S PET	BROWNNOSER	CHOCOLATE MILK

EACH YEAR IN THE UNITED STATES, OVER A HUNDRED KIDS ARE NAMED UNIQUE.

Careers IN Mischief

"I ALWAYS ARRIVE LATE AT THE OFFICE, BUT I MAKE UP FOR IT BY LEAVING EARLY." —Charles Lamb

It's never too early to start thinking about your future career.[1] If you like mischief, you can wreak havoc at almost any job, but firefighters probably have the best reputation as practical jokers. They have a lot of time to kill between emergency calls, and a person's mind just naturally turns to mischief when it's not

---

1. If you are retired, please ignore that statement.

occupied with waxing fire trucks and coiling hoses.

Another place you might enjoy working is at the Department of Motor Vehicles (DMV). There you will get to test people who come in to take driving tests. This puts you in a position of authority with someone who is afraid of you. You're in the driver's seat![2] Below are some of the silly comments people have given their DMV examiners during their driving tests. Imagine the fun!

"HOW DO YOU START THIS THING?"

"MY LAST FOUR EXAMINERS WERE MEAN. YOU LOOK NICE."

"I HAVEN'T DRIVEN IN TWENTY YEARS. I'VE BEEN IN PRISON A WHILE."

"I'VE NEVER DRIVEN THIS CAR BEFORE."

---

2. Actually, it's the passenger seat. But you get to hold a clipboard and everything!

"MY MOM SAID I WASN'T READY FOR THIS. DO YOU THINK I'M READY? I NEED YOU TO THINK I'M READY."

If you are a real mischief maker, you won't go for a really good job. Instead, you'll torture your parents by getting a horrible one. Think of their disappointment! Of course, you'll also want a job that can challenge your mighty intellect, so it's lucky for you that *Popular Science* ranked the Ten Worst Jobs in Science. These jobs include the position of whale-feces researcher. Your work would include

collecting whale dung and looking carefully through it. Practice shouting "Brown stain, ahoy!" now to get an edge on the other candidates.

If you're a *CSI* watcher, you may prefer the job of forensic entomologist. These are the detectives who help solve murders by analyzing the maggots, cheese skippers, and other insects found in decaying bodies.

YOU'LL BE SAYING THINGS LIKE "THESE CORPSE MAGGOTS ARE GOING TO HELP ME GET SOME BAD GUYS OFF THE STREET."

Along with a possible career in garbage-ology (studying garbage) and elephant vasectomy (neutering really big animals), you may also want to consider becoming a hazardous materials diver. This job involves putting on a diving suit and then swimming in sewage, through toxic spills, and inside nuclear reactors. (You can also wear the diving suit if someone pees in the pool.)

ONE JOB THAT EVEN THE MOST DEDICATED MISCHIEF MAKER HAS TO BE GLAD IS NO LONGER AVAILABLE IS THAT OF "ARMPIT PLUCKER." THIS WAS THE PERSON IN ANCIENT ROME WHOSE WORK INVOLVED TWEEZING AND THEN LISTENING TO THE HIDEOUS SCREAMING OF HIS CUSTOMERS.

What other modern jobs hold the potential for mischief? My neighbor once told me that astronauts sometimes reprogram satellites to burn a fiery path of destruction as they crash-land into populated areas. (And don't even get me started about lawyers or the folks at the petting zoo!) But whatever choice you make, rest assured that with the skills you've learned in this book, you'll make a mark in whatever your future career might be.

The End

(Or is it?)

ACKNOWLEDGMENTS

I had hoped that these people could be held legally liable for this book's contents, but my counsel informs me that this is not possible. Nevertheless, some of the discredit for this book should fall upon Lynn King, Suzanne Taylor, Austin and Dan Sharp, Tom Booth, Janet and Michael King, Doug Levin, Arthur Digbee, Blair Ellis, Peter King, Kyle Edmister, Michael "5 percent body fat" Milone, Uncle Edgester, Andy Lennox, Geoffrey Simmons, M.D., Sean Mackin, June Yi, Kathleen Twomey, Linda Holt, Jim Murai, Andy Lipson, Cindy and Erik "the Greater" King, Peter Clark, Lorraine Miller, Thad Mepham, Jeff McCallum, Bruno Lernout, Courtney Rottgering, Kris "Gus" King, and Jared Smith.

And to Brody vanderSommen: You know what I want to say, man.[1]

---

1. !#$@%&!?

Ananova.com. "Anti-New Year protest." January 2, 2007.

Applebom, Peter. "A Zen Master's Heart, a Rock-Paper-Scissors Hand." *New York Times*, November 26, 2006.

BadVibes. http://www.sound101.org/

"Best April, Fools Ever!" *Girls Life*, April 2006.

Black, Edward. "Dictionary Shows Why It's Easier to Be Nasty Than Nice." *News.Scotsman.com*, August 10, 2005. http://news.scotsman.com/uk.cfm?id=1755032005

Boese, Alex. The Museum of Hoaxes. http://www.museumofhoaxes.com/

Bryson, Bill. *A Short History of Nearly Everything*. New York: Broadway Books, 2003.

Clayman, Steven E. "Booing: The Anatomy of a Disaffiliative Response." *American Sociological Review*, February 1993.

"Crime and puckishness." *Civilization*, August/September 1996.

Crystal, David. *Words, Words, Words*. Oxford University Press, 2006.

Cuddihy, Paul. "Mascots' foul play anything but lucky." *Sunday Herald*, November 19, 2000.

Daley, Jason. "The Worst Jobs in Science 2007." *Popular Science*, June 2007.

"Eaten Missionary's Family Gets Apology." *BBC News*, November 13, 2003. http://news.bbc.co.uk/2/hi/asia-pacific/3263163.stm

Ehrlich, Jay. "How to give a wedgie." *Cosmo Girl*, April 2004.

Evans, Bruce, Bill Flavin, and Jennifer Hart. "The Style Invitational: Week 231: Giving Quarter." *Washington Post*, August 17, 1997.

Forstchen, William R. "The Burning of Beards." *It Seemed Like a Good Idea . . .* New York: Harper-Collins, 2000.

Freely, I. Poo. *Involuntary Bowel Motility and You*. Pocatello, Idaho: Spelunker Books, 1971.

"From Hermes to bonsai kittens." *Economist*, December 24, 2005.

Garland, Shannon. "Eat Me,' Says Chile's Controversial Artist Marco Evaristti." *Santiago Times*, January 7, 2007.

"German Man Falls off Balcony in 'Spit for Distance' Competition." *Der Spiegel*, June 1, 2007.

Gorman, James. "Does This Mean People Turned Off, Tuned Out, and Dropped In?" *New York Times*, June 27, 2006.

Griffiths, Andy. (Er, I've read *all* his books, and I think you should, too.)

"Half the world will be gazing." *Economist*, May 16, 1992.

Halle, Kay. *Irrepressible Churchill*. London: Robson Books, 2003.

Hallman, Tom, Jr. "Queen of passenger seat rules the roads." *Oregonian*, December 28, 2006.

Hattikudur, Mangesh, ed., with Elizabeth Hunt and Will Pearson. *Mental Floss Presents: Forbidden Knowledge*. New York: Collins, 2005.

Howard, Lucy, and others. "www.I Grabbed Your Name.com." *Newsweek*, April 17, 2000.

Jaffe, Al. *Snappy Answers to Stupid Questions*. New York: Warner Books, 1975.

Kiefer, Peter. "In Italian Town, a Civics Lesson From Pelting Neighbors." *New York Times*, February 19, 2007.

Kim, Albert, Kostya Kennedy, and George Plimpton. "Sidd Finch Lives!" *Sports Illustrated*, April 1, 2002.

Klein, Matthew. *Con Ed*. New York: Warner Books, 2007.

Landal, James. *The Last Duel: A True Story of Death and Honour*. Edinburgh, Scotland: Canongate, 2006.

Leone, Vicki. *Working IX to V*. New York: Walker & Company, 2007.

Letcher, Piers. "A Continental Christmas." *Guardian Unlimited*, November 17, 2005. http://www.guardian .co.uk/travel/2005/nov/17/culturaltrips.travelfood anddrink.foodanddrink

Lincoln Museum site. http://www.thelincolnmuseum .org/

Lyall, Sarah. "Book Lovers Seek Lovers, Buttered or Plain." *New York Times*, November 21, 2006.

Masoff, Joy. *Oh, Yikes! History's Grossest, Wackiest Moments*. New York: Workman, 2006.

Morgan, Richard. "Reverse Graffiti." *New York Times Magazine*, December 10, 2006.

Morgan, Tim. Guide to Shooting Rubber Bands. http://members.aol.com/morganbolt/main.html

Myth Busters: Don't Try This at Home. San Francisco: Jossey-Bass, 2006.

"Choice of Name Upsets Officials." *Sky News*, August 16, 2007. http://news.sky.com/skynews/article/0,,91059-1280203,00.html

Peterson, T. F. *Nightwork: A History of Hacks and Pranks at MIT*. MIT Press, 2003.

Plimpton, George. "The Curious Case of Sidd Finch." *Sports Illustrated*, April 1, 1985.

"Power surge explodes 'superloo.'" *BBC News*, February 4, 2004. http://news.bbc.co.uk/1/hi/england/staffordshire/3457965.stm

Pranks.com. http://www.pranks.com

Reid, Luc. *Talk the Talk: The Slang of 65 American Subcultures*. Cincinnati, Ohio: Writer's Digest Books, 2006.

Roberts, David, ed. *Pick Me Up*. New York: DK Publishing, 2006.

Romero, Simon. "Venezuelan Parents Love a Famous Name." *New York Times*, January 7, 2007.

Rose, David, ed. *They Call Me Naughty Lola*. New York: Scribner, 2006.

Schott, Ben. *Schott's Sporting, Gaming, & Idling Miscellany*. New York: Bloomsbury, 2005.

———. *Schott's Almanac: 2007*. New York: Bloomsbury, 2006.

Sjöberg, Lore. "Grading Norse Gods." *Day to Day*, National Public Radio, August 25, 2003.

Slansky, Paul, and Arleen Sorkin. *My Bad: 25 Years of Public Apologies*. New York: Bloomsbury, 2006.

Smith, Robert. "NYC Hosts Olympics for Sewer Workers." National Public Radio, *Morning Edition*, May 9, 2007.

Steinberg, Neil. *If at All Possible, Involve a Cow*. New York: St. Martin's Press, 1992.

Stream, Golden. *Downward Spiral: Richard Nixon's Favorite Toilets*. Whittier, California: Republican Press Limited, 1974.

Sussman, Paul. "Europe: A continent of bizarre sporting endeavour." *http://www.cnn.com*.

Turpin, Adrian. "The Lost Olympians." *Independent*, August 8, 2004.

"Twelve urban pranks." *Spy*, February 1994.

Urban Dictionary.com. http://www.urbandictionary .com/

Wakin, Daniel J. "The High C and the Low Rumble." *New York Times*, December 17, 2006.

The Web Gone MAD. http://www.leedberg.com/mad/

Weisman, Jon. "Groening's a mild child gone wild." *Variety*, May 16, 2007.

Wex, Michael. *Born to Kvetch: Yiddish Language and Culture in All of Its Moods*. New York: St. Martin's Press, 2005.

Whimsy, Lord Breaulove Swells. *The Affected Provincial's Companion, Volume One*. New York: Bloomsbury, 2006.

Zachs, Richard. *An Underground Education*. New York: Doubleday, 1997.

Zimmerman, Kent and Keith. *Myth Busters: The Explosive Truth*. New York: Simon & Schuster Entertainment, 2005.